AS Maths
AQA Core 1

AS level maths is seriously tricky — no question about that.

We've done everything we can to make things easier for you.
We've scrutinised past paper questions and we've gone through the syllabuses with a fine-toothed comb. So we've found out exactly what you need to know, then explained it simply and clearly.

We've stuck in as many helpful hints as you could possibly want
— then we even tried to put some funny bits in to keep you awake.

We've done our bit — the rest is up to you.

What CGP is all about

Our sole aim here at CGP is to produce the highest quality books — carefully written, immaculately presented and dangerously close to being funny.

Then we work our socks off to get them out to you
— at the cheapest possible prices.

Contents

SECTION 5 — DIFFERENTIATION

SECTION 6 — INTEGRATION

P1 — PRACTICE EXAM 1

P1 — PRACTICE EXAM 2

This book covers the Core 1 module of the AQA specification.

Published by Coordination Group Publications Ltd.

Contributors:
Charley Darbishire
Simon Little
Andy Park
Glenn Rogers
Mike Smith
Claire Thompson
Kieran Wardell

And:
Iain Nash

Updated by:
Tim Major
Sam Norman
Ali Palin
Andy Park
Alice Shepperson
Claire Thompson
Julie Wakeling

With thanks to Colin Wells and Ann Francis for the proofreading.

ISBN: 978 1 84146 764 1

Groovy website: www.cgpbooks.co.uk

Jolly bits of clipart from CorelDRAW®
Printed by Elanders Hindson Ltd, Newcastle upon Tyne.

Based on the classic CGP style created by Richard Parsons.

A Few Definitions and Things

Yep, this is a pretty dull way to start a book. A list of definitions. But in the words of that annoying one-hit wonder bloke in the tartan suit, things can only get better. Which is nice.

Polynomials

POLYNOMIALS are expressions of the form $a + bx + cx^2 + dx^3 + ...$

$5y^3 + 2y + 23$ — Polynomial in the variable y.

$1 + x^2$

$z^{42} + 3z - z^2 - 1$ — Polynomial in the variable z.

The bits separated by the +/– signs are <u>terms</u>.

x, y and z are always VARIABLES
They're usually what you solve equations to find. They often have more than one possible value.

Letters like a, b, c are always CONSTANTS
Constants never change. They're fixed numbers — but can be represented by letters. π is a good example. You use the symbol π, but it's just a number = 3.1415...

Functions

FUNCTIONS take a value, do something to it, and output another value.

$f(x) = x^2 + 1$ — function f takes a value, squares it and adds 1.

$g(x) = 2 - \sin 2x$ — function g takes a value (in degrees), doubles it, takes the sine of it, then takes the value away from 2.

You can plug values into a function — just replace the variable with a certain number.

$f(-2) = (-2)^2 + 1 = 5$

$f(0) = (0)^2 + 1 = 1$

$f(252) = (252)^2 + 1 = 63505$

$g(-90) = 2 - \sin(-180°) = 2 - 0 = 2$

$g(0) = 2 - \sin 0° = 2 - 0 = 2$

$g(45) = 2 - \sin 90° = 2 - 1 = 1$

Exam questions use functions all the time. They generally don't have that much to do with the actual question. It's just a bit of terminology to get comfortable with.

Multiplication and Division

There's three different ways of showing MULTIPLICATION:

1) with good old-fashioned "times" signs (×):

$f(x) = (2x \times 6y) + (2x \times \sin x) + (z \times y)$

The multiplication signs and the variable x are easily confused.

2) or sometimes just use a little dot:

$f(x) = 2x.6y + 2x.\sin x + z.y$

Dots are better for long expressions — they're less confusing and easier to read.

3) but you often don't need anything at all:

$f(x) = 12xy + 2x \sin x + zy$

And there's three different ways of showing DIVISION:

1) $\dfrac{x+2}{3}$

2) $(x+2) \div 3$

3) $(x+2)/3$

Equations and Identities

This is an IDENTITY:

$$x^2 - y^2 \equiv (x + y)(x - y)$$

But this is an EQUATION:

$$y = x^2 + x$$

Make up any values you like for x and y, and it's always true. The left-hand side always equals the right-hand side.

This has at most two possible solutions for each value of y. e.g. if y=0, x can only be 0 or -1.

The difference is that the identity's true for <u>all</u> values of x and y, but the equation's only true for certain values.

NB: If it's an identity, use the $\equiv$ sign instead of $=$.

Surds

A surd is a number like $\sqrt{2}$, $\sqrt[3]{12}$ or $5\sqrt{3}$ — one that's written with the $\sqrt{}$ sign. They're important because you can give <u>exact</u> answers where you'd otherwise have to round to a certain number of decimal places.

Surds are sometimes the only way to give an *Exact Answer*

Put $\sqrt{2}$ into a calculator and you'll get something like 1.414213562...
But square 1.414213562 and you get 1.999999999.

And no matter how many decimal places you use, you'll never get <u>exactly</u> 2.
The only way to write the exact, spot on value is to <u>use surds</u>.

There are basically **Three Rules** *for using* **Surds**

There are three <u>rules</u> you'll need to know to be able to use surds properly. Check out the 'Rules of Surds' box below.

EXAMPLES: (i) Simplify $\sqrt{12}$ and $\sqrt{\frac{3}{16}}$.   (ii) Show that $\frac{9}{\sqrt{3}} = 3\sqrt{3}$.   (iii) Find $\left(2\sqrt{5} + 3\sqrt{6}\right)^2$.

(i) <u>Simplifying</u> surds means making the number in the $\sqrt{}$ sign <u>smaller</u>, or getting rid of a <u>fraction</u> in the $\sqrt{}$ sign.

$$\sqrt{12} = \sqrt{4 \times 3} = \sqrt{4} \times \sqrt{3} = 2\sqrt{3} \qquad \sqrt{\frac{3}{16}} = \frac{\sqrt{3}}{\sqrt{16}} = \frac{\sqrt{3}}{4}$$

Using $\sqrt{\frac{a}{b}} = \frac{\sqrt{a}}{\sqrt{b}}$.

Using $\sqrt{ab} = \sqrt{a}\sqrt{b}$.

(ii) For questions like these, you have to write a number (here, it's 3) as $3 = \left(\sqrt{3}\right)^2 = \sqrt{3} \times \sqrt{3}$.

$$\frac{9}{\sqrt{3}} = \frac{3 \times 3}{\sqrt{3}} = \frac{3 \times \sqrt{3} \times \sqrt{3}}{\sqrt{3}} = 3\sqrt{3}$$

Cancelling $\sqrt{3}$ from the top and bottom lines.

(iii) Multiply surds very <u>carefully</u> — it's easy to make a silly mistake.

$$\left(2\sqrt{5} + 3\sqrt{6}\right)^2 = \left(2\sqrt{5} + 3\sqrt{6}\right)\left(2\sqrt{5} + 3\sqrt{6}\right)$$
$$= \left(2\sqrt{5}\right)^2 + 2 \times \left(2\sqrt{5}\right) \times \left(3\sqrt{6}\right) + \left(3\sqrt{6}\right)^2$$
$$= \left(2^2 \times \sqrt{5}^2\right) + \left(2 \times 2 \times 3 \times \sqrt{5} \times \sqrt{6}\right) + \left(3^2 \times \sqrt{6}^2\right)$$
$$= 20 + 12\sqrt{30} + 54$$
$$= 74 + 12\sqrt{30}$$

$= 4 \times 5 = 20$ $= 12\sqrt{5}\sqrt{6} = 12\sqrt{30}$ $= 9 \times 6 = 54$

Rules of Surds

There's not really very much to remember.

$$\sqrt{ab} = \sqrt{a}\sqrt{b}$$
$$\sqrt{\frac{a}{b}} = \frac{\sqrt{a}}{\sqrt{b}}$$
$$a = \left(\sqrt{a}\right)^2 = \sqrt{a}\sqrt{a}$$

Remove surds from the bottom of fractions by **Rationalising the Denominator**

Surds are pretty darn complicated. So they're the last thing you want at the bottom of a fraction.

But have no fear — <u>Rationalise the Denominator</u>...
Yup, you heard... (it means getting rid of the surds from the bottom of a fraction).

EXAMPLE: Rationalise the denominator of $\frac{1}{1+\sqrt{2}}$

Multiply the top and bottom by the denominator (but change the sign in front of the surd).

This works because:
$(a+b)(a-b) = a^2 - b^2$

$$\frac{1}{1+\sqrt{2}} \times \frac{1-\sqrt{2}}{1-\sqrt{2}}$$
$$\frac{1-\sqrt{2}}{\left(1+\sqrt{2}\right)\left(1-\sqrt{2}\right)} = \frac{1-\sqrt{2}}{1^2+\sqrt{2}-\sqrt{2}-\sqrt{2}^2}$$
$$\frac{1-\sqrt{2}}{1-2} = \frac{1-\sqrt{2}}{-1} = -1 + \sqrt{2}$$

Surely the pun is mightier than the surd...

There's not much to surds really — but they cause a load of hassle. Think of them as just ways to save you the bother of getting your calculator out and pressing buttons — then you might grow to know and love them. The box of rules in the middle is the vital stuff. Learn them till you can write them down without thinking — then get loads of practice with them.

Taking Out Common Factors

Common factors need to be hunted down, and taken outside the brackets. They are a danger to your exam mark.

Spot those Common Factors

A bit which is in each term of an expression is a <u>common factor</u>.

> ### Spot Those Common Factors $\quad 2x^3z + 4x^2yz + 14x^2y^2z$ ◄── Look for any bits that are in each term.
>
> <u>Numbers:</u>   there's a common factor of 2 here because 2 divides into 2, 4 and 14.
>
> <u>Variables:</u>   there's at least an x^2 in each term and there's a z in each term.
>
> So there's a <u>common factor of 2x²z</u> in this expression.

And Take Them Outside a Bracket

If you spot a common factor you can "<u>take it out</u>":

Write the common factor outside a bracket. ➔ $\quad 2x^2z\left(x + 2y + 7y^2\right)$

and put what's left of each term inside the bracket:

Afterwards, always <u>multiply back out</u> to check you did it right:

Check by Multiplying Out Again

$$2x^2z\left(x + 2y + 7y^2\right) = 2x^3z + 4x^2yz + 14x^2y^2z$$

But it's not just numbers and variables you need to look for...

Trig Functions: $\quad \sin x \sin y + \cos x \sin y$

This has a common factor of sin y. So take it out to get...

$$\sin y\left(\sin x + \cos x\right)$$

Brackets: $\quad (y+a)^2(x-a)^3 + (x-a)^2$

$(x-a)^2$ is a common factor — it comes out to give:

$$(x-a)^2\left((y+a)^2(x-a) + 1\right)$$

Look for Common Factors when Simplifying Expressions

> **EXAMPLE:**   Simplify... $\quad (x+1)(x-2) + (x+1)^2 - x(x+1)$
>
> There's an (x+1) factor in each term, so we can <u>take this out as a common factor</u> (hurrah).
>
> $$(x+1)\{(x-2) + (x+1) - x\}$$
>
> The terms inside the big bracket are the old terms with an (x+1) removed.
>
> At this point you should check that this multiplies out to give the original expression. (You can just do this in your head, if you trust it.)
>
> Then simplify the big bracket's innards:
>
> $$(x+1)(x - 2 + x + 1 - x)$$
>
> Get this answer by multiplying out the two brackets (or by using the "difference of two squares").
>
> $$= (x+1)(x-1)$$
>
> $$= x^2 - 1$$

Bored of spotting trains or birds? Try common factors...

You'll be doing this business of taking out common factors a lot — so get your head round this. It's just a case of looking for things that are in all the different terms of an expression, i.e. bits they have in common. And if something's in all the different terms, save yourself some time and ink, and write it once — instead of two, three or more times.

Multiplying Out Brackets

In this horrific nightmare that is AS-level maths, you need to manipulate and simplify expressions all the time.

Remove brackets by Multiplying them out

Here's the basic types you have to deal with. You'll have seen them before. But there's no harm in reminding you, eh?

Multiply Your Brackets Here — we do all shapes and sizes

Single Brackets

$$a(b+c+d)=ab+ac+ad$$

Squared Brackets

$$(a+b)^2=(a+b)(a+b)=a^2+2ab+b^2$$

Use the middle stage until you're comfortable with it. Just _never_ make this _mistake_: $(a+b)^2=a^2+b^2$

Double Brackets

$$(a+b)(c+d)=ac+ad+bc+bd$$

Long Brackets

Write it out again with each term from one bracket separately multiplied by the other bracket.

$$(x+y+z)(a+b+c+d)$$
$$=x(a+b+c+d)+y(a+b+c+d)+z(a+b+c+d)$$

Then multiply out each of these brackets, one at a time.

Single Brackets

$$3xy(x^2+2x-8)$$

Multiply all the terms inside the brackets by the bit outside — separately.

$$(3xy\times x^2)+(3xy\times 2x)+(3xy\times(-8))$$

I've put brackets round each bit to make it easier to read.

All the stuff in the brackets now needs sorting out. Work on each bracket separately.

$$(3x^3y)+(6x^2y)+(-24xy)$$

Multiply the numbers first, then put the x's and other letters together.

$$3x^3y+6x^2y-24xy$$

Squared Brackets

Either write it as two brackets and multiply it out...

$$(2y^2+3x)^2$$
$$(2y^2+3x)(2y^2+3x)$$

The dot just means 'mulitiplied by' — the same as the × sign.

$$2y^2.2y^2+2y^2.3x+3x.2y^2+3x.3x$$

From here on it's simplification — nothing more, nothing less.

$$4y^4+6xy^2+6xy^2+9x^2$$
$$4y^4+12xy^2+9x^2$$

...or do it in one go.

$$(2y^2)^2+2(2y^2)(3x)+(3x)^2$$
$$a^2 \qquad 2ab \qquad b^2$$
$$4y^4+12xy^2+9x^2$$

Long Brackets

$$(2x^2+3x+6)(4x^3+6x^2+3)$$

Each term in the first bracket has been multiplied by the second bracket.

$$2x^2(4x^3+6x^2+3)+3x(4x^3+6x^2+3)+6(4x^3+6x^2+3)$$

Now multiply out each of these brackets.

$$(8x^5+12x^4+6x^2)+(12x^4+18x^3+9x)+(24x^3+36x^2+18)$$

Then simplify it all...

$$8x^5+24x^4+42x^3+42x^2+9x+18$$

Go forth and multiply out brackets...

OK, so this is obvious, but I'll say it anyway — if you've got 3 or more brackets together, multiply them out 2 at a time. Then you'll be turning a really hard problem into two easy ones. You can do that loads in maths. In fact, writing the same thing in different ways is what maths is about. That and sitting in classrooms with tacky 'maths can be fun' posters...

SECTION ONE — ALGEBRA BASICS

Algebraic Fractions

No one likes fractions. But just like Mondays, you can't put them off forever. Face those fears. Here goes...

The first thing you've got to know about fractions:

$$\frac{a}{x} + \frac{b}{x} + \frac{c}{x} \equiv \frac{a+b+c}{x}$$

You can just add the stuff on the top lines because the bottom lines are all the same.

x is called a common denominator — a fancy way of saying 'the bottom line of all the fractions is x'.

Add fractions by putting them over a **Common Denominator**...

Finding a common denominator just means 'rewriting some fractions so all their bottom lines are the same'.

EXAMPLE: Simplify $\frac{1}{2x} - \frac{1}{3x} + \frac{1}{5x}$

You need to rewrite these so that all the bottom lines are equal. What you want is something that all these bottom lines divide into.

Put It over a Common Denominator

30 is the lowest number that 2, 3, and 5 go into. So the common denominator is 30x.

$$\frac{15}{30x} - \frac{10}{30x} + \frac{6}{30x}$$

Always check that these divide out to give what you started with.

$$= \frac{15 - 10 + 6}{30x} = \frac{11}{30x}$$

...even **horrible** looking ones

Yep, finding a common denominator even works for those fraction nasties — like these:

EXAMPLE: Simplify $\frac{2y}{x(x+3)} + \frac{1}{y^2(x+3)} - \frac{x}{y}$

Find the Common Denominator

Take all the individual 'bits' from the bottom lines and multiply them together. Only use each bit once unless something on the bottom line is squared.

The individual 'bits' here are x, (x+3) and y...

$$xy^2(x+3)$$

...but you need to use y^2 because there's a y^2 in the second fraction's denominator.

Put Each Fraction over the Common Denominator

Make the denominator of each fraction into the common denominator.

$$\frac{y^2 \times 2y}{y^2 x(x+3)} + \frac{x \times 1}{xy^2(x+3)} - \frac{xy(x+3) \times x}{xy(x+3)y}$$

Multiply the top and bottom lines of each fraction by whatever makes the bottom line the same as the common denominator.

Combine into One Fraction

Once everything's over the common denominator — you can just add the top lines together.

$$= \frac{2y^3 + x - x^2 y(x+3)}{xy^2(x+3)}$$

As always — if you see a minus sign, look out for possible problems.

All the bottom lines are the same — so you can just add the top lines.

$$= \frac{2y^3 + x - x^3 y - 3x^2 y}{xy^2(x+3)}$$

All you need to do now is tidy up the top.

Not the nicest of answers. But it _is_ the answer, so it'll have to do.

Well put me over a common denominator and pickle my walrus...

Adding fractions — turning lots of fractions into one fraction. Sounds pretty good to me, since it means you don't have to write as much. Better do it carefully, though — otherwise you can watch those marks shoot straight down the toilet.

Simplifying Expressions

I know this is basic stuff but if you don't get really comfortable with it you <u>will</u> make silly mistakes. You will.

Cancelling stuff on the top and bottom lines

Cancelling stuff is good — because it means you've got rid of something, and you don't have to write as much.

EXAMPLE: Simplify $\dfrac{ax+ay}{az}$

You can do this in two ways. Use whichever you prefer — but make sure you understand the ideas behind both.

Factorise — then Cancel

$$\frac{ax+ay}{az}=\frac{a(x+y)}{az}$$

Factorise the top line.

Cancel the 'a'. $\Rightarrow \dfrac{\cancel{a}(x+y)}{\cancel{a}z}=\dfrac{x+y}{z}$

Split into Two Fractions — then Cancel

$$\frac{ax+ay}{az}=\frac{ax}{az}+\frac{ay}{az}$$

This is an okay thing to do — just think what you'd get if you added these.

$$=\frac{\cancel{a}x}{\cancel{a}z}+\frac{\cancel{a}y}{\cancel{a}z}=\frac{x}{z}+\frac{y}{z}$$

This answer's the same as the one from the first box — honest. Check it yourself by adding the fractions.

Simplifying complicated-looking Brackets

EXAMPLE: Simplify the expression $(x-y)(x^2+xy+y^2)$

There's only one thing to do here.... Multiply out those brackets!

$$(x-y)(x^2+xy+y^2)=x(x^2+xy+y^2)-y(x^2+xy+y^2)$$
$$=(x^3+x^2y+xy^2)-(x^2y+xy^2+y^3)$$
$$=x^3+x^2y+xy^2-x^2y-xy^2-y^3$$

Multiplying each term in the first bracket by the second bracket.

Multiplying out each of these two brackets.

Don't forget these become minus signs because of the minus sign in front of the bracket.

And then the x²y and the xy² terms disappear...

$$=x^3-y^3$$

Sometimes you just have to do Anything you can think of and Hope...

Sometimes it's not easy to see what you're supposed to do to simplify something. When this happens — just do anything you can think of and see what 'comes out in the wash'.

EXAMPLE: Simplify $4x+\dfrac{4x}{x+1}-4(x+1)$

There's nothing obvious to do — so do what you can. Try adding them as fractions...

$$4x+\frac{4x}{x+1}-4(x+1)=\frac{(x+1)\times4x}{x+1}+\frac{4x}{x+1}-\frac{(x+1)\times4(x+1)}{x+1}$$

The common denominator is (x + 1).

$$=\frac{4x^2+4x+4x-4(x+1)^2}{x+1}$$

Still looks horrible. So work out the brackets — but don't forget the minus signs.

$$=\frac{4x^2+4x+4x-4x^2-8x-4}{x+1}$$
$$=-\frac{4}{x+1}$$

Aha — everything disappears to leave you with this. And this is definitely simpler than it looked at the start.

Don't look at me like that...

Choose a word, any word at all. Like "Simple". Now stare at it. Keep staring at it. Does it look weird? No? Stare a bit longer. Now does it look weird? Yes? Why is that? I don't understand.

Factorising a Quadratic

It's not over yet...

Factorising a quadratic when a ≠ 1

These can be a real pain. The basic method's the same as on the previous page — but it can be a bit more awkward.

EXAMPLE: Factorise $3x^2 + 4x - 15$

A — Write Down Two Brackets

As before, write down two brackets — but instead of just having x in each, you need two things that will multiply to give $3x^2$.

$$3x^2 + 4x - 15 = (3x\quad)(x\quad)$$

It's got to be $3x$ and x here.

B — The Fiddly Bit

You need to find two numbers that multiply together to make 15 — but which will give you 4x when you multiply them by x and 3x, and then add / subtract them.

$(3x\quad1)(x\quad15) \Rightarrow x$ and $45x$ which then add or subtract to give 46x and 44x.

$(3x\quad15)(x\quad1) \Rightarrow 15x$ and $3x$ which then add or subtract to give 18x and 12x.

$(3x\quad3)(x\quad5) \Rightarrow 3x$ and $15x$ which then add or subtract to give 18x and 12x.

$(3x\quad5)(x\quad3) \Rightarrow 5x$ and $9x$ which then add or subtract to give 14x and 4x.

This is the value you're after — so this is the right combination.

C — Add the Signs

You know the brackets must be like these... $\Rightarrow (3x\quad5)(x\quad3) = 3x^2 + 4x - 15$

So all you have to do is put in the plus or minus signs.

c is negative — that means the signs in the brackets are different.

$(3x+5)(x-3) = 3x^2 - 4x - 15$

or...

$(3x-5)(x+3) = 3x^2 + 4x - 15$ ⇐ So it's this one.

You've only got two choices — if you're unsure, just multiply them out to see which one's right.

Sometimes it's best just to **Cheat** and use the **Formula**

Here's two final points to bear in mind:

1) It won't always factorise.

2) Sometimes factorising is so messy that it's easier to just use the quadratic formula...

So if the question doesn't tell you to factorise, don't assume it will factorise.
And if it's something like this thing below, don't bother trying to factorise it...

EXAMPLE: Solve $6x^2 + 87x - 144 = 0$

This will actually factorise, but there's 2 possible bracket forms to try.

$(6x\quad)(x\quad)$ or $(3x\quad)(2x\quad)$ And for each of these, there's 8 possible ways of making 144 to try.

And you can quote me on that...

"He who can properly do quadratic equations is considered a god."
Plato

"Quadratic equations are the music of reason."
James J Sylvester

Completing the Square

Completing the Square is a handy little trick that you should <u>definitely</u> know how to use.
It can be a bit fiddly — but it gives you <u>loads</u> of information about a quadratic really quickly.

Take any old quadratic and put it in a **Special Form**

Completing the square can be really confusing. For starters, what does "Completing the Square" <u>mean</u>?
<u>What</u> is the square? <u>Why</u> does it need completing? Well, there is <u>some</u> logic to it:

1) The <u>square</u> is something like this: $(x+\text{something})^2$ It's basically the factorised equation (with the factors both the same), but there's something missing...

2) ...So you need to 'complete' it by adding a number to the square to make it equal to the original equation. $(x+\text{something})^2 + d$

You'll start with something like this...   ...sort the x-coefficients...   ...and you'll end up with something like this.

$$2x^2 + 8x - 5 \quad \Longrightarrow \quad 2(x+2)^2 + ? \quad \Longrightarrow \quad 2(x+2)^2 - 13$$

Lovely!

Make completing the square a bit **Easier**

There are only a few stages to completing the square — if you can't be bothered trying to understand it,
just <u>learn how to do it</u>. But I reckon it's worth spending a bit more time to get your head round it <u>properly</u>.

A

Take Out a Factor of 'a'

— take a factor of a out of the x^2 and x terms.

$f(x) = 2x^2 + 3x - 5$ ← This is in the form $ax^2 + bx + c$

This '2' is an 'a'.

$f(x) = 2\left(x^2 + \frac{3}{2}x\right) - 5$ ← Check that the bracket multiplies out to what you had before.

This is $\frac{b}{a}$

B

Rewrite the Bracket — rewrite the bracket as one bracket squared.

The number in the brackets is <u>always</u> half the old number in front of the x. $\dfrac{b}{2a}$

$f(x) = 2\left(x + \frac{3}{4}\right)^2 + d$ ← d is a number you have to find to make the new form equal to the old one.

Don't forget the 'squared' sign.

C

Complete the Square — find d.

To do this, <u>make the old and new equations equal each other</u>...

...and you can find d.

The x^2 and x bits are the same on both sides so they can disappear.

$$2\left(x+\frac{3}{4}\right)^2 + d = 2x^2 + 3x - 5$$

$$2x^2 + 3x + \frac{9}{8} + d = 2x^2 + 3x - 5$$

$$\frac{9}{8} + d = -5$$

$$\Rightarrow d = -\frac{49}{8}$$

Completing the Square

A) <u>**THE BIT IN THE BRACKETS IS ALWAYS**</u> — $a\left(x + \dfrac{b}{2a}\right)^2$

B) <u>**CALL THE NUMBER AT THE END d**</u> — $a\left(x + \dfrac{b}{2a}\right)^2 + d$

C) <u>**MAKE THE TWO FORMS EQUAL**</u> — $ax^2 + bx + c = a\left(x + \dfrac{b}{2a}\right)^2 + d$

D

So the Answer is: $f(x) = 2x^2 + 3x - 5 = 2\left(x + \frac{3}{4}\right)^2 - \frac{49}{8}$

Complete your square — it'd be root not to...

Remember — you're basically trying to write the expression as one bracket squared, but it doesn't quite work. So you have
to add a number (d) to make it work. It's a bit confusing at first, but once you've learnt it you won't forget it in a hurry.

Completing the Square

Once you've completed the square, you can very quickly say loads about a quadratic function. And most of it relies on the fact that a squared number can never be less than zero... ever.

Completing the square can sometimes be Useful

This is a quadratic written as a completed square. As it's a quadratic function and the coefficient of x^2 is positive, it's a u-shaped graph.

This is a square — it can never be negative. The smallest it can be is 0.

$$f(x) = 3x^2 - 6x - 7 = 3(x-1)^2 - 10$$

A **Find the Minimum** — make the bit in the brackets equal to zero.

When the squared bit is zero, f(x) reaches its minimum value. This means the graph reaches its lowest point.

$$f(x) = 3(x-1)^2 - 10$$

This number here is the minimum.

$$f(1) = 3(1-1)^2 - 10$$

f(1) means using x=1 in the function

$$f(1) = 3(0)^2 - 10 = -10$$

So the minimum is -10, when x=1

B **Where Does f(x) Cross the x-axis?**

Make the completed square function equal zero.

$$3(x-1)^2 - 10 = 0$$

Solve it to find where f(x) crosses the x-axis.

$$\Rightarrow (x-1)^2 = \frac{10}{3}$$

da-de-dah ... rearranging again.

$$\Rightarrow x - 1 = \pm\sqrt{\frac{10}{3}}$$

$$\Rightarrow x = 1 \pm \sqrt{\frac{10}{3}}$$

So f(x) crosses the x-axis when...

$$x = 1 + \sqrt{\frac{10}{3}} \ or \ 1 - \sqrt{\frac{10}{3}}$$

These notes are all about graphs with positive coefficients in front of the x^2. But if the coefficient is negative, then the graph is flipped upside-down (n-shaped, not u-shaped).

With this information, you can easily sketch the graph...

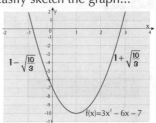

$1 - \sqrt{\frac{10}{3}}$ $1 + \sqrt{\frac{10}{3}}$ $f(x)=3x^2 - 6x - 7$

Some functions don't have Real Roots

By completing the square, you can also quickly tell if the graph of a quadratic function ever crosses the x-axis. It'll only cross the x-axis if the function changes sign (i.e. goes from positive to negative or vice versa). Take this function...

Find the Roots $f(x) = x^2 + 4x + 7$

This number's positive.

$$f(x) = (x+2)^2 + 3$$

The smallest this bit can be is zero (at x = –2).

$(x + 2)^2$ is never less than zero so f(x) is never less than three.

This means that:
a) f(x) can never be negative.
b) The graph of f(x) never crosses the x-axis.

You can think of a completed square as two Translations of an x^2 graph

$y = (x + a)^2$ Writing 'x + a' instead of 'x' means the graph moves sideways by a.
1) If a > 0, the graph goes to the left.
2) If a < 0, the graph goes to the right.

$y = (x + a)^2 + b$ Adding a number to the whole function shifts the graph up or down by b.
1) If b > 0, the graph goes upwards.
2) If b < 0, the graph goes downwards.

Don't forget — two wrongs don't make a root...

You'll be pleased to know that that's the end of me trying to tell you how to do something you probably really don't want to do. Now you can push it to one side and run off to roll around in a bed of nettles... much more fun.

The Quadratic Formula

Unlike factorising, the quadratic formula always works... no ifs, no buts, no butts, no nothing...

The **Quadratic Formula** — a reason to be cheerful, but careful...

If you want to solve a quadratic equation $ax^2 + bx + c = 0$, then the answers are given by this formula:

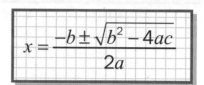

$$x = \frac{-b \pm \sqrt{b^2 - 4ac}}{2a}$$

The formula's a godsend — but use the power wisely...

> If any of the coefficients (i.e. if a, b or c) in your quadratic equation are negative — be <u>especially</u> careful.

> Always take things nice and <u>slowly</u> — don't try to rush it.

> It's a good idea to write down what a, b and c are <u>before</u> you start plugging them into the formula.

> There are a couple of minus signs in the formula — which can catch you out if you're not paying <u>attention</u>.

I shall teach you the ways of the **Formula**

EXAMPLE: Solve the quadratic equation $3x^2 - 4x = 8$. Leave your answer in surd form.

The mention of surds is a <u>big</u> clue that you should use the formula.

✦A✦ Rearrange the Equation

Get the equation in the standard $ax^2 + bx + c = 0$ form.

$$3x^2 - 4x = 8$$
$$3x^2 - 4x - 8 = 0$$

✦B✦ Find a, b and c

Write down the coefficients a, b and c — making sure you don't forget minus signs.

$$3x^2 - 4x - 8 = 0$$
$$a = 3 \qquad b = -4 \qquad c = -8$$

✦C✦ Stick Them in the Formula

Very carefully, plug these numbers into the formula. It's best to write down each stage as you do it.

$$x = \frac{-b \pm \sqrt{b^2 - 4ac}}{2a}$$

$$= \frac{-(-4) \pm \sqrt{(-4)^2 - 4 \times 3 \times (-8)}}{2 \times 3}$$

$$= \frac{4 \pm \sqrt{16 + 96}}{6}$$

$$= \frac{4 \pm \sqrt{112}}{6}$$

The ± sign means that we have two different expressions for x — which you get by replacing the ± with + and –.

$$= \frac{4 \pm 4\sqrt{7}}{6}$$

Since $\sqrt{112} = \sqrt{16} \times \sqrt{7}$

$$x = \frac{2}{3} + \frac{2}{3}\sqrt{7} \ or \ \frac{2}{3} - \frac{2}{3}\sqrt{7}$$

Using this magic formula, I shall take over the world... ha ha ha...

Okay, maybe it's not <u>quite</u> that good... but it's really important. So learn it properly — which means spending enough time until you can just say it out loud the whole way through, with no hesitations. Or perhaps you could try singing it as loud as you can to the tune of your favourite cheesy song. Sha-la-la-la-la-la-la-ha... La-di-da... Sha-la-la-la-la-la-la-ha... La-di-da... Sha-la-la-la-la-la-la-ha...

The Quadratic Formula

By using part of the quadratic formula, you can quickly tell if a quadratic equation has two solutions, one solution, or no solutions at all. Tell me more, I hear you cry...

How Many Roots? Check the $b^2 - 4ac$ bit...

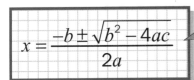

$$x = \frac{-b \pm \sqrt{b^2 - 4ac}}{2a}$$

When you try to find the roots of a quadratic function, this bit in the square-root sign ($b^2 - 4ac$) can be positive, zero, or negative. It's <u>this</u> that tells you if a quadratic function has two roots, one root, or no roots.

The $b^2 - 4ac$ bit is called the <u>discriminant</u>.

<u>Because</u> — if the discriminant is positive, the formula will give you two different values — when you add or subtract the $\sqrt{b^2 - 4ac}$ bit.

<u>But</u> if it's zero, you'll only get one value, since adding or subtracting zero doesn't make any difference.

<u>And</u> if it's negative, you don't get any (real) values because you can't take the square root of a negative number.

Well, not in Core 1. In later modules, you can actually take the square root of negative numbers and get 'imaginary' numbers. That's why we say no 'real' roots — because there are 'imaginary' roots!

It's good to be able to picture what this means:

A root is just when y = 0, so it's where the graph touches or crosses the x-axis.

$b^2 - 4ac > 0$	$b^2 - 4ac = 0$	$b^2 - 4ac < 0$
Two roots	One root	No roots

So the graph crosses the x-axis twice and these are the roots:

The graph just touches the x-axis from above (or from below if the x^2 coefficient is negative).

The graph doesn't touch the x-axis at all.

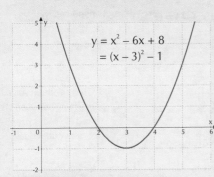

$y = x^2 - 6x + 8$
$= (x - 3)^2 - 1$

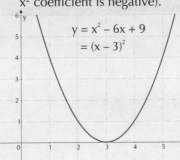

$y = x^2 - 6x + 9$
$= (x - 3)^2$

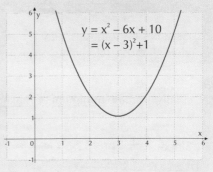

$y = x^2 - 6x + 10$
$= (x - 3)^2 + 1$

EXAMPLE: Find the range of values of k for which: a) f(x)=0 has 2 distinct roots, b) f(x)=0 has 1 root, c) f(x) has no real roots, where $f(x) = 3x^2 + 2x + k$.

First of all, work out what the discriminant is:
$b^2 - 4ac = 2^2 - 4 \times 3 \times k$
$= 4 - 12k$

These calculations are exactly the same. You don't need to do them if you've done a) because the only difference is the equality symbol.

a) <u>Two distinct roots</u> means:
$b^2 - 4ac > 0 \Rightarrow 4 - 12k > 0$
$\Rightarrow 4 > 12k$
$\Rightarrow k < \frac{1}{3}$

b) <u>One root</u> means:
$b^2 - 4ac = 0 \Rightarrow 4 - 12k = 0$
$\Rightarrow 4 = 12k$
$\Rightarrow k = \frac{1}{3}$

c) <u>No roots</u> means:
$b^2 - 4ac < 0 \Rightarrow 4 - 12k < 0$
$\Rightarrow 4 < 12k$
$\Rightarrow k > \frac{1}{3}$

ha ha ha ha haaaaaa... ha ha ha... ha ha ha ... ha ha ha........

So for questions about "how many roots", think discriminant — i.e. $b^2 - 4ac$. And don't get the inequality signs (> and <) the wrong way round. It's obvious, if you think about it.

Sketching Quadratic Graphs

If a question doesn't seem to make sense, or you can't see how to go about solving a problem, try drawing a <u>graph</u>. It sometimes helps if you can actually <u>see</u> what the problem is, rather than just reading about it.

Sketch the graphs of the following quadratic functions:

① $y = 2x^2 - 4x + 3$

② $y = 8 - 2x - x^2$

Quadratic graphs are **Always** u-shaped or n-shaped

 The first thing you need to know is whether the graph's going to be u-shaped or n-shaped (upside down). To decide, look at the <u>coefficient of x^2</u>.

$y = 2x^2 - 4x + 3$

The coefficient of x^2 here is <u>positive</u>... ...so the graph's u-shaped. → +ve

$y = 8 - 2x - x^2$

The coefficient of x^2 here is <u>negative</u>... ...so the graph's upside down (n-shaped). → –ve

 Now find the places where the graph crosses the <u>axes</u> (both the y-axis and the x-axis).

(i) Put x=0 to find where it meets the <u>y-axis</u>.

$y = 2x^2 - 4x + 3$

$y = (2 \times 0^2) - (4 \times 0) + 3$ so $y = 3$ ← That's where it crosses the y-axis

(ii) Solve y=0 to find where it meets the <u>x-axis</u>.

$2x^2 - 4x + 3 = 0$

$b^2 - 4ac = -8 < 0$ ← You could use the formula. But first check $b^2 - 4ac$ to see if y = 0 has any roots.

So it has no solutions, and doesn't cross the x-axis.

For more info, see page 13.

(i) Put x=0.

$y = 8 - 2x - x^2$

$y = 8 - (2 \times 0) - 0^2$ so $y = 8$

(ii) Solve y=0.

$8 - 2x - x^2 = 0$ ← This equation factorises easily...

$\Rightarrow (2 - x)(x + 4) = 0$

$\Rightarrow x = 2 \ or \ x = -4$

C Finally, find the <u>minimum</u> or <u>maximum</u> (i.e. the <u>vertex</u>).

Since $y = 2(x - 1)^2 + 1$ ← By <u>completing the square</u> (see page 10).

the minimum value is $y = 1$, which occurs at $x = 1$

The minimum or maximum of the graph is always at $x = \frac{-b}{2a}$

The maximum value is <u>halfway</u> between the roots — the graph's symmetrical.

The maximum value is at $x = -1$

So the maximum is $y = 8 - (2 \times -1) - (-1)^2$

i.e. the graph has a maximum at the point (–1,9).

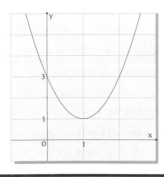

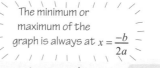

Sketching Quadratic Graphs

A) <u>up or down</u> — decide which direction the curve points in.

B) <u>axes</u> — find where the curve crosses them.

C) <u>max / min</u> — find the turning point.

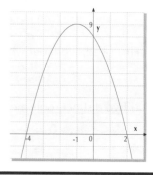

Van Gogh, Monet — all the greats started out sketching graphs...

So there's three steps here to learn. Simple enough. You can do the third step (finding the max/min point) by either a) completing the square, which is covered a bit later, or b) using the fact that the graph's symmetrical — so once you've found the points where it crosses the x-axis, the point halfway between them will be the max/min. It's all laughs here...

Algebraic Division and the Remainder Theorem

Algebraic division — Mmmm, fun it's not. It's something you have to know, though —
so if you can't do it yet, get on and learn it. Then you can move on to brighter things.

Do **Polynomial Division** by means of **Subtraction**

$$(2x^3 - 3x^2 - 3x + 7) \div (x - 2) = ?$$

The trick with this is to see how many times you can subtract $(x-2)$ from $2x^3 - 3x^2 - 3x + 7$.
The idea is to keep subtracting lumps of $(x-2)$ until you've got rid of all the powers of x.

Do the subtracting in **Stages**

At each stage, always try to get rid of the highest power of x.
Then start again with whatever you've got left.

① Start with $2x^3 - 3x^2 - 3x + 7$, and subtract $2x^2$ lots of $(x-2)$ to get rid of the x^3 term.

$$(2x^3 - 3x^2 - 3x + 7) - 2x^2(x-2)$$
$$(2x^3 - 3x^2 - 3x + 7) - 2x^3 + 4x^2$$
$$= x^2 - 3x + 7$$

$2x^3 \div x = 2x^2$

This is what's left — so now you have to get rid of the x^2 term.

② Now start again with $x^2 - 3x + 7$.
The highest power of x is the x^2 term.
So subtract x lots of $(x-2)$ to get rid of that.

$$(x^2 - 3x + 7) - x(x-2)$$
$$(x^2 - 3x + 7) - x^2 + 2x$$
$$= -x + 7$$

Now start again with this — and get rid of the x term.

③ All that's left now is $-x + 7$.
Get rid of the $-x$ by subtracting -1 times $(x-2)$.

$$(-x + 7) - (-1(x-2))$$
$$(-x + 7) + x - 2$$
$$= 5$$

There are no more powers of x to get rid of — so stop here.

The remainder's 5.

Interpreting the results...

Time to work out exactly what all that meant.

Started with: $2x^3 - 3x^2 - 3x + 7$
Subtracted: $2x^2(x-2) + x(x-2) - 1(x-2)$
$$= (x-2)(2x^2 + x - 1)$$
Remainder: $= 5$

So... $2x^3 - 3x^2 - 3x + 7 = (x-2)(2x^2 + x - 1) + 5$

or... $\dfrac{2x^3 - 3x^2 - 3x + 7}{(x-2)} = 2x^2 + x - 1$ with remainder 5.

Algebraic Division

$$(ax^3 + bx^2 + cx + d) \div (x - k) = ?$$

1) SUBTRACT a multiple of $(x-k)$ to get rid of the highest power of x.

2) REPEAT step 1 until you've got rid of all the powers of x.

3) WORK OUT how many lumps of $(x-k)$, you've subtracted, and the REMAINDER.

The **Remainder Theorem** is an easy way to work out **Remainders**

When you divide $f(x)$ by $(x - a)$, the remainder is $f(a)$.

So in the example above, you could have worked out the remainder dead easily.

1) $f(x) = 2x^3 - 3x^2 - 3x + 7$.
2) You're dividing by $(x-2)$, so $a = 2$.
3) So the remainder must be $f(2) = (2 \times 8) - (3 \times 4) - (3 \times 2) + 7 = 5$.

Careful now... when you're dividing by something like $(x+7)$, a is negative — so here, $a = -7$.

Factor Theorem

The factor theorem is fantastic — no doubt about it. It can really help you factorise cubics. But not only that, at this week's special CGP price of only £27.49*, thanks to its twin rotating blades, it allows a closer factorisation than ever before. So for smoother, closer, and faster factorising, choose the CGP Fantastic Factor Theorem every time.

Feel the power of the *Factor Theorem*

The Factor Theorem's dead useful, and is certainly going to be of use come the exam. And don't forget it's fantastic.

> ### The Fantastic Factor Theorem:
>
> If f(x) is a polynomial, and f(a) = 0, then (x – a) is a factor of f(x).
>
> In other words: If you know the roots, you also know the factors — and vice versa.

EXAMPLE: Show that $(x+1)$ is a factor of $f(x) = x^3 + 4x^2 - 7x - 10$

The question's giving you a <u>big</u> hint here. If you show that f(–1) = 0, then the factor theorem says that (x + 1) is a factor.

$$f(x) = x^3 + 4x^2 - 7x - 10$$

$$f(-1) = -1 + 4 + 7 - 10 = 0$$

So, by the factor theorem, (x+1) is a factor of f(x).

See pages 8-9 for more on factorising.

You can use the Factor Theorem when *x* has a **coefficient** other than 1

You might be asked to show that (ax – b) (i.e. something with a number in front of the x) is a factor of a polynomial. But don't start panicking just yet — you can still use the factor theorem.

EXAMPLE: Show that $(2x-1)$ is a factor of $f(x) = 2x^2 - 9x + 4$

Notice that 2x – 1 = 0 when x = ½. Plug this value of x into f(x).

$$f(x) = 2x^2 - 9x + 4$$

$$f\left(\tfrac{1}{2}\right) = 2\left(\tfrac{1}{2}\right)^2 - \left(9 \times \tfrac{1}{2}\right) + 4$$

$$f\left(\tfrac{1}{2}\right) = \tfrac{1}{2} - \tfrac{9}{2} + 4 = 0$$

So by the factor theorem, (x – ½) is a factor.
And if that's a factor, then 2 (x – ½) = (2x – 1) is also a factor†.

†Explanation of a tricky bit...

If you <u>multiply</u> one factor by a number, you've got to <u>divide</u> the other factor by the <u>same number</u>.

e.g.
$$f(x) = \left(x - \tfrac{1}{2}\right)(p)$$
$$f(x) = (2x-1)\left(\tfrac{1}{2}p\right)$$

e.g.
$$8 \times 6 = 48$$
$$(8 \times 3)(6 \div 3) = 48$$
$$(24)(2) = 48$$

(x–1) is a **Factor** if the coefficients add up to **0**

This is a useful thing to remember.
It works for all polynomials — no exceptions.
It could save a fair whack of time in the exam.

EXAMPLE: Factorise the polynomial $f(x) = 6x^2 - 7x + 1$

The coefficients (6, –7 and 1) add up to 0. That means f(1) = 0. And that applies to <u>any polynomial</u> at all... always.

So by the factor theorem, if f (1) = 0, (x – 1) is a factor. Easy.

Just factorise it like an easy quadratic to get this:

$$f(x) = 6x^2 + 1 = (6x-1)(x-1)$$

* Plus Postage and Packaging, at £28.49. Allow at least 28 months for delivery.

You've lost that Factor Theorem, whoah, yeah that Factor Theorem...

You know, I had NO idea how great a factor I could get. Not until I tried CGP's Fantastic Factor Theorem.
I used to have problems with factorisation when dating, and in my general life. But now I've put all that behind me.
Now I've got the confidence to talk about factors wherever I go. I can really experience the joy of factorising.
And it's all thanks to CGP's Fantastic Factor Theorem: Try it today — it changed my life, and it could change yours too.

Factorising Cubics

Factorising a quadratic function is okay — but you might also be asked to factorise a cubic (something with x^3 in it). And that takes a bit more time — there are more steps, so there are more chances to make mistakes.

Factorising a cubic given **One Factor**

$$f(x) = 2x^3 + x^2 - 8x - 4$$

Factorising a cubic means exactly what it meant with a quadratic — putting brackets in.
When they ask you to factorise a cubic expression, they'll usually tell you one of the factors.

> **EXAMPLE:** Given that $(x + 2)$ is a factor of $f(x) = 2x^3 + x^2 - 8x - 4$, express f(x) as the product of three linear factors.

① The first step is to find a quadratic factor. So write down the factor you know, along with another set of brackets.

$$(x+2)(\qquad) = 2x^3 + x^2 - 8x - 4$$

Put the x^2 bit in this new set of brackets.
These have to <u>multiply together</u> to give you this.

$$(x+2)(2x^2 \qquad) = 2x^3 + x^2 - 8x - 4$$

② Find the number for the second set of brackets. These have to <u>multiply together</u> to give you this.

$$(x+2)(2x^2 \quad -2) = 2x^3 + x^2 - 8x - 4$$

③ These multiplied give you $-2x$, but there's $-8x$ in f(x) — so you need an 'extra' $-6x$. And that's what this $-3x$ is for.

$$(x+2)(2x^2 - 3x - 2) = 2x^3 + x^2 - 8x - 4$$

You only need $-3x$ because it's going to be multiplied by 2, which makes $-6x$.

If you wanted to solve a cubic, you'd do it <u>exactly</u> the same way — put it in the form $ax^3 + bx^2 + cx + d = 0$ and factorise.

Factorising Cubics

1) **Find a factor, (if you need to) by finding $f(0)$, $f(\pm 1)$, $f(\pm 2)$,... until you find $f(k) = 0$. Then $(x - k)$ is a factor.**

2) **Put in the x^2 term.**

3) **Put in the constant.**

4) **Put in the x term by comparing the number of x's on both sides.**

5) **Check there are the same number of x^2's on both sides.**

6) **Factorise the quadratic you've found — if that's possible.**

④ Before you go any further, check that there are the same number of x^2's on <u>both</u> sides.

$4x^2$ from here...

$$(x+2)(2x^2 - 3x - 2) = 2x^3 + x^2 - 8x - 4$$

...and $-3x^2$ from here... ...add together to give this x^2.

If this is okay, factorise the quadratic into two linear factors.

$$(2x^2 - 3x - 2) = (2x + 1)(x - 2)$$

And so... $\quad 2x^3 + x^2 - 8x - 4 = (x+2)(2x+1)(x-2)$

Factorising a cubic given **No Factors**

If they don't give you the first factor, you have to find it <u>yourself</u>. But it's okay — they'll give you an easy one. The best way to find a factor is to <u>guess</u> — use trial and error.

> **Find f(1)** If the answer is zero, you know $(x - 1)$ is a factor.
> If the answer isn't zero, find $f(-1)$. If that's zero, then $(x + 1)$ is a factor.

If that doesn't work, keep trying small numbers (find $f(2)$, $f(-2)$, $f(3)$, $f(-3)$ and so on) until you find a number that gives you <u>zero</u> when you put it in the <u>cubic</u>. Call that number k.

$(x - k)$ is a <u>factor of the cubic</u> (from the Factor Theorem).

I love the smell of fresh factorised cubics in the morning...

Factorising cubics is exactly the same as learning to unicycle... It's impossible at first. But when you finally manage it, it's really easy from then onwards and you'll never forget it. Probably. To tell the truth, I can't unicycle at all. So don't believe a word I say.

Section Two Revision Questions

Mmmm, well, quadratic equations — not exactly designed to make you fall out of your chair through laughing so hard, are they? But (and that's a huge 'but') they'll get you plenty of marks come that fine morning when you march confidently into the exam hall — if you know what you're doing. And what better way to make sure you know what you're doing than to practise. So here we go then, on the thrill-seekers' ride of a lifetime — the CGP quadratic equation revision section...

1) Factorise the following expressions. While you're doing this, sing a jolly song to show how much you enjoy it.
   a) $x^2 + 2x + 1$,
   b) $x^2 - 13x + 30$,
   c) $x^2 - 4$,
   d) $3 + 2x - x^2$
   e) $2x^2 - 7x - 4$,
   f) $5x^2 + 7x - 6$.

2) Solve the following equations. And sing verse two of your jolly song.
   a) $x^2 - 3x + 2 = 0$,
   b) $x^2 + x - 12 = 0$,
   c) $2 + x - x^2 = 0$,
   d) $x^2 + x - 16 = x$
   e) $3x^2 - 15x - 14 = 4x$,
   f) $4x^2 - 1 = 0$,
   g) $6x^2 - 11x + 9 = 2x^2 - x + 3$.

3) Rewrite these quadratics by completing the square. Then state their maximum or minimum value and the value of x where this occurs. Also, say which ones cross the x-axis — just for a laugh, like.
   a) $x^2 - 4x - 3$,
   b) $3 - 3x - x^2$,
   c) $2x^2 - 4x + 11$,
   d) $4x^2 - 28x + 48$.

4) How many roots do these quadratics have? Sketch their graphs.
   a) $x^2 - 2x - 3 = 0$,
   b) $x^2 - 6x + 9 = 0$,
   c) $2x^2 + 4x + 3 = 0$.

5) Solve these quadratic equations, leaving your answers in surd form.
   a) $3x^2 - 7x + 3 = 0$,
   b) $2x^2 - 6x - 2 = 0$,
   c) $x^2 + 4x + 6 = 12$.

6) If the quadratic equation $x^2 + kx + 4 = 0$ has two real roots, what are the possible values of k?

7) Do the following algebraic divisions. What are the remainders?
   a) $(x^3 - 2x^2 + 6x + 12) \div (x + 2)$
   b) $(3x^3 + 7x^2 - 2x - 1) \div (x - 1)$.

8) Show that $(x + 2)$ is a factor of $x^3 + 5x^2 + 2x - 8$.

9) a) Show that $(3x - 1)$ is a factor of $3x^3 + 23x^2 + 37x - 15$.
   b) Factorise $x^3 - x^2 - 4x + 4$ into three factors.

OK, I think that's enough. Go and make yourself a cup of tea. Treat yourself to a chocolate biscuit.

Here is a new way to enjoy Pelican biscuits:

Bite a small piece off two opposite corners of a Pelican.
Immerse one corner in coffee, and suck coffee up through the Pelican, like a straw. You will need to suck quite hard to start with.
After a few seconds you will notice the biscuit part of the Pelican start to lose structural integrity. At this point, cram it into your mouth, where it will collapse into a mass of hot molten chocolate, biscuit and coffee.

Mmmm.

Linear Inequalities

Solving inequalities is very similar to solving equations. You've just got to be really careful that you keep the inequality sign pointing the right way.

> Find the ranges of x that satisfy these inequalities:
> (i) $x - 3 < -1 + 2x$ (ii) $8x + 2 \geq 2x + 17$ (iii) $4 - 3x \leq 16$ (iv) $36x < 6x^2$

Sometimes the inequality sign Changes Direction

Like I said, these are pretty similar to solving equations — because whatever you do to one side, you have to do to the other. But multiplying or dividing by negative numbers changes the direction of the inequality sign.

Adding or Subtracting doesn't change the direction of the inequality sign

EXAMPLE: If you add or subtract something from both sides of an inequality, the inequality sign doesn't change direction.

Adding 1 to both sides leaves the inequality sign pointing in the same direction.

Subtracting x from both sides doesn't affect the inequality.

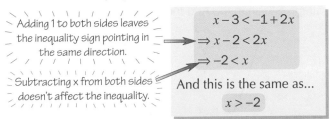

$$x - 3 < -1 + 2x$$
$$\Rightarrow x - 2 < 2x$$
$$\Rightarrow -2 < x$$

And this is the same as...

$$x > -2$$

Multiplying or Dividing by something Positive doesn't affect the inequality sign

EXAMPLE: Multiplying or dividing both sides of an inequality by a positive number doesn't affect the direction of the inequality sign.

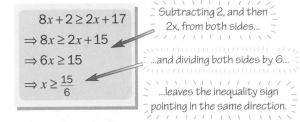

$$8x + 2 \geq 2x + 17$$
$$\Rightarrow 8x \geq 2x + 15$$
$$\Rightarrow 6x \geq 15$$
$$\Rightarrow x \geq \frac{15}{6}$$

Subtracting 2, and then 2x, from both sides...

...and dividing both sides by 6...

...leaves the inequality sign pointing in the same direction.

But Change the inequality if you Multiply or Divide by something Negative

But multiplying or dividing both sides of an inequality by a negative number changes the direction of the inequality.

EXAMPLE:
$$4 - 3x \leq 16$$
$$\Rightarrow -3x \leq 12$$
$$\Rightarrow x \geq -4$$

Subtract 4 from both sides.

Then divide both sides by -3 — but change the direction of the inequality.

> The reason for the sign changing direction is because it's just the same as swapping everything from one side to the other:
> $$-3x \leq 12 \Rightarrow -12 \leq 3x \Rightarrow x \geq -4$$

Don't divide both sides by Variables — like x and y

You've got to be really careful when you divide by things that might be negative — well basically, don't do it.

EXAMPLE: $36x < 6x^2$

Start by dividing by 6.

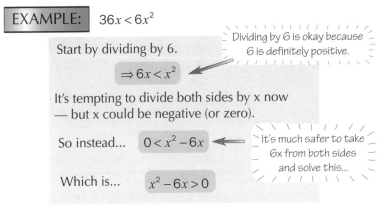

$$\Rightarrow 6x < x^2$$

Dividing by 6 is okay because 6 is definitely positive.

It's tempting to divide both sides by x now — but x could be negative (or zero).

So instead... $0 < x^2 - 6x$

It's much safer to take 6x from both sides and solve this...

Which is... $x^2 - 6x > 0$

Two types of inequality sign

There are two kinds of inequality sign:

Type 1: $<$ — less than
          $>$ — greater than

Type 2: $\leq$ — less than or equal to
          $\geq$ — greater than or equal to

Whatever type the question uses — use the same kind all the way through your answer.

See the next page for more on solving quadratic inequalities.

So no one knows we've arrived safely — splendid...

So just remember — inequalities are just like normal equations except that you have to reverse the sign when multiplying or dividing by a negative number. And don't divide both sides by variables. (You should know not to do this with normal equations anyway because the variable could be zero.) OK — lecture's over.

Quadratic Inequalities

With quadratic inequalities, you're best off drawing the graph and taking it from there.

Draw a **Graph** to solve a **Quadratic** inequality

Example: Find the ranges of x which satisfy these inequalities:

$$\text{(1)} \quad -x^2 + 2x + 4 \geq 1 \qquad\qquad \text{(2)} \quad 2x^2 - x - 3 > 0$$

First rewrite the inequality with <u>zero</u> on one side.

$$-x^2 + 2x + 3 \geq 0$$

Then <u>draw</u> the graph of $y = -x^2 + 2x + 3$:

So find where it crosses the x-axis (i.e. where y=0):

$$-x^2 + 2x + 3 = 0 \implies x^2 - 2x - 3 = 0$$
$$\implies (x+1)(x-3) = 0$$
$$\implies x = -1 \text{ or } x = 3$$

And the coefficient of x^2 is negative, so the graph is n-shaped. So it looks like this:

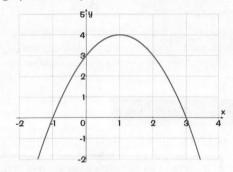

You're interested in when this is <u>positive or zero</u>, i.e. when it's above the x-axis.

From the graph, this is when x is <u>between –1 and 3</u> (including those points). So your answer is...

$$-x^2 + 2x + 4 \geq 1 \text{ when } -1 \leq x \leq 3.$$

This one already has zero on one side, so <u>draw</u> the graph of $y = 2x^2 - x - 3$.

Find where it crosses the x-axis:

$$2x^2 - x - 3 = 0$$
$$\implies (2x - 3)(x + 1)$$
$$\implies x = \tfrac{3}{2} \text{ or } x = -1$$

Factorise it to find the roots.

And the coefficient of x^2 is positive, so the graph is u-shaped. And looks like this:

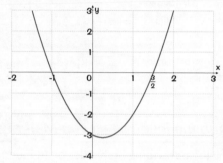

You need to say when this is <u>positive</u>. Looking at the graph, there are two parts of the x-axis where this is true — when x is <u>less than –1</u> and when x is <u>greater than 3/2</u>. So your answer is:

$$2x^2 - x - 3 > 0 \text{ when } x < -1 \text{ or } x > \tfrac{3}{2}.$$

Example (revisited): On the last page you had to solve $36x < 6x^2$.

$$36x < 6x^2$$
$$\text{equation 1} \implies 6x < x^2$$
$$\implies 0 < x^2 - 6x$$

So draw the graph of

$$y = x^2 - 6x = x(x - 6)$$

And this is <u>positive</u> when $x < 0$ or $x > 6$.

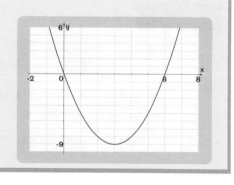

If you divide by x in equation 1, you'd only get half the solution — you'd miss the $x < 0$ part.

That's nonsense — I can see perfectly...

Call me sad, but I reckon these questions are pretty cool. They look a lot more difficult than they actually are and you get to draw a picture. Wow! When you do the graph, the important thing is to find where it crosses the x-axis (you don't need to know where it crosses the y-axis) and make sure you draw it the right way up. Then you just need to decide which bit of the graph you want. It'll either be the range(s) of x where the graph is below the x-axis or the range(s) where it's above. And this depends on the inequality sign.

Simultaneous Equations

Solving simultaneous equations means finding the answers to two equations <u>at the same time</u> — i.e. finding values for x and y for which both equations are true. And it's one of those things that you'll have to do <u>again and again</u> — so it's definitely worth practising them until you feel <u>really confident</u>.

① $3x + 5y = -4$
② $-2x + 3y = 9$

This is how simultaneous equations are usually shown. It's a good idea to label them as equation① and equation② — so you know which one you're working with.

But they'll look different sometimes, maybe like this. $\longrightarrow$ $4 + 5y = -3x$ $\quad$ rearrange as $ax + by = c$ $\quad$ $3x + 5y = -4$
Make sure you rearrange them as 'ax + by = c'. $\quad\quad -2x = 9 - 3y$ $\longrightarrow$ $-2x + 3y = 9$

Solving them by *Elimination*

Elimination is a lovely method. It's really quick when you get the hang of it — you'll be doing virtually all of it in your head.

EXAMPLE:

① $\quad 3x + 5y = -4$
② $\quad -2x + 3y = 9$

To get the x's to match, you need to multiply the first equation by 2 and the second by 3:

①×2 $\quad 6x + 10y = -8$
②×3 $\quad -6x + 9y = 27$

Add the resulting equations together to eliminate the x's.

$$19y = 19$$
$$y = 1$$

So y is 1. Now stick that value for y into one of the equations to find x:

$y = 1$ in ① $\Rightarrow 3x + 5 = -4$
$$3x = -9$$
$$x = -3$$

So the solution is x = –3, y = 1.

But you should always...

{A} Match the Coefficients

Multiply the equations by numbers that will make either the x's or the y's match in the two equations. (Ignoring minus signs.)

Go for the lowest common multiple (LCM). e.g. LCM of 2 and 3 is 6.

{B} Eliminate to Find One Variable

If the coefficients are the <u>same</u> sign, you'll need to <u>subtract</u> one equation from the other.

If the coefficients are <u>different</u> signs, you need to <u>add</u> the equations.

{C} Find the Variable You Eliminated

When you've found one variable, put its value into one of the original equations so you can find the other variable.

{D} Check Your Answer

...by putting these values into the other equation.

② $-2x + 3y = 9$
$x = -3$
$y = 1$

$-2 \times (-3) + 3 \times 1 = 6 + 3 = 9$

If these two numbers are the same, then the values you've got for the variables are right.

Elimination Method

1) **Match the coefficients**
2) **Eliminate and then solve for one variable**
3) **Find the other variable (that you eliminated)**
4) **Check your answer**

Eliminate your social life — do AS-level maths

This is a fairly basic method that won't be new to you. So make sure you know it. The only possibly tricky bit is matching the coefficients — work out the lowest common multiple of the coefficients of x, say, then multiply the equations to get this number in front of each x.

22

Simultaneous Equations with Quadratics

Elimination is great for simple equations. But it won't always work. Sometimes one of the equations has not just x's and y's in it — but bits with x^2 and y^2 as well. When this happens, you can <u>only</u> use the <u>substitution</u> method.

Use Substitution if one equation is *Quadratic*

EXAMPLE: $\quad -x + 2y = 5$ —Ⓛ ← The <u>linear</u> equation — with only x's and y's in.

$\qquad\qquad\quad x^2 + y^2 = 25$ —Ⓠ ← The <u>quadratic</u> equation — with some x^2 and y^2 bits in.

Rearrange the <u>linear equation</u> so that either x or y is on its own on one side of the equals sign.

$$Ⓛ \quad -x + 2y = 5$$
$$\Rightarrow x = 2y - 5$$

Substitute this expression into the <u>quadratic equation</u>...

$$\text{Sub into } Ⓠ: \quad x^2 + y^2 = 25$$
$$\Rightarrow (2y - 5)^2 + y^2 = 25$$

...and then rearrange this into the form $ax^2 + bx + c = 0$, so you can solve it — either by <u>factorising</u> or using the <u>quadratic formula</u>.

$$\Rightarrow (4y^2 - 20y + 25) + y^2 = 25$$
$$\Rightarrow 5y^2 - 20y = 0$$
$$\Rightarrow 5y(y - 4) = 0$$
$$\Rightarrow y = 0 \text{ or } y = 4$$

One Quadratic and One Linear Eqn

1) **Isolate variable in linear equation**
   Rearrange the linear equation to get either x or y on its own.

2) **Substitute into quadratic equation**
   — to get a quadratic equation in just one variable.

3) **Solve to get values for one variable**
   — either by factorising or using the quadratic formula.

4) **Stick these values in the linear equation**
   — to find corresponding values for the other variable.

Finally put both these values back into the <u>linear equation</u> to find corresponding values for x:

When y = 0: $\quad -x + 2y = 5$ Ⓛ
$$\Rightarrow x = -5$$

When y = 4: $\quad -x + 2y = 5$ Ⓛ
$$\Rightarrow -x + 8 = 5$$
$$\Rightarrow x = 3$$

So the solutions to the simultaneous equations are: x = –5, y = 0 and x = 3, y = 4.

As usual, <u>check your answers</u> by putting these values back into the original equations.

Check Your Answers

x = –5, y = 0: $\quad -(-5) + 2 \times 0 = 5$ ✓
$$(-5)^2 + 0^2 = 25 ✓$$

x = 3, y = 4: $\quad -(3) + 2 \times 4 = 5$ ✓
$$3^2 + 4^2 = 25 ✓$$

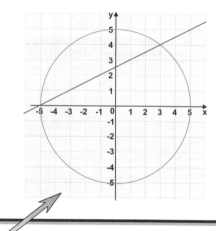

$y = x^2$ — a match-winning substitution...

The quadratic equation above is actually a <u>circle</u> about the origin with radius 5. (Don't worry, the pages about circles come later in the book — see Section 4 for more info). The linear equation is just a standard straight line. So what you're actually finding here are the two points where the line passes through the circle. And these turn out to be (–5,0) and (3,4). See the graph. (I thought you might appreciate seeing a graph that wasn't a line or a parabola for a change.)

Geometric Interpretation

When you have to interpret something <u>geometrically</u> — you have to draw a picture and 'say what you see'.

Two Solutions — Two points of Intersection

Example:
$$y = x^2 - 4x + 5 \quad \text{①}$$
$$y = 2x - 3 \quad \text{②}$$

Solution: Substitute expression for y from ② into ①:
$$2x - 3 = x^2 - 4x + 5$$

Rearrange and solve:
$$x^2 - 6x + 8 = 0$$
$$(x-2)(x-4) = 0$$
$$x = 2 \text{ or } x = 4$$

In ② gives:
$$x = 2 \Rightarrow y = 2\times2 - 3 = 1$$
$$x = 4 \Rightarrow y = 2\times4 - 3 = 5$$

There's 2 pairs of solutions: x=2, y=1 and x=4, y=5

Geometric Interpretation:

So from solving the simultaneous equations, you know that the graphs meet in <u>two places</u> — the points (2,1) and (4,5).

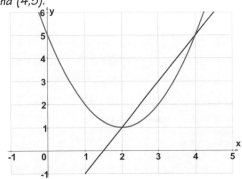

One Solution — One point of Intersection

Example:
$$y = x^2 - 4x + 5 \quad \text{①}$$
$$y = 2x - 4 \quad \text{②}$$

Solution: Substitute ② in ①:
$$2x - 4 = x^2 - 4x + 5$$

Rearrange and solve:
$$x^2 - 6x + 9 = 0$$
$$(x-3)^2 = 0$$
$$x = 3$$

Double root i.e. you only get 1 solution from the quadratic.

In Equation ② gives:
$$y = 2\times3 - 4$$
$$y = 2$$

There's 1 solution: x=3, y=2

Geometric Interpretation:

Since the equations have only one solution, the two graphs only meet at one point — (3,2). The straight line is a <u>tangent</u> to the curve.

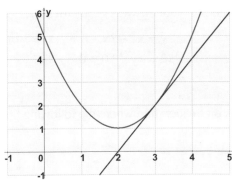

No Solutions means the Graphs Never Meet

Example:
$$y = x^2 - 4x + 5 \quad \text{①}$$
$$y = 2x - 5 \quad \text{②}$$

Solution: Substitute ② in ①:
$$2x - 5 = x^2 - 4x + 5$$

Rearrange and try to solve with the quadratic formula:
$$x^2 - 6x + 10 = 0$$
$$b^2 - 4ac = (-6)^2 - 4.10$$
$$= 36 - 40 = -4$$

$b^2 - 4ac < 0$, so the quadratic has no real roots.
So the simultaneous equations have no real solutions.

Geometric Interpretation:

The equations have no solutions — the graphs never meet.

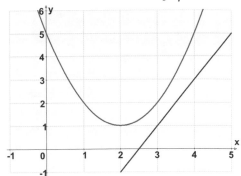

Geometric Interpretation? Frankly my dear, I don't give a damn...

There's some lovely practice Simultaneous Equations questions on the next page.

Section Three Revision Questions

What's that I hear you cry? You want revision questions — and lots of them. Well, it just so happens I've got a few here. Lots of questions on the different kinds of inequalities you need to know about, plus simultaneous equations. Now, as far as quadratic inequalities go, my advice is, 'if you're not sure, draw a picture — even if it's not accurate'. And as for simultaneous equations — well, just don't rush them — or you'll spend twice as long looking for milkshakes mistakes as it took you to do the question in the first place. That's it, the advice is over. So on with the questions...

1) Solve a) $7x - 4 > 2x - 42$, b) $12y - 3 \le 4y + 4$,   c) $9y - 4 \ge 17y + 2$.

2) Find the ranges of x that satisfy these inequalities: i) $x + 6 < 5x - 4$ ii) $4x - 2 > x - 14$ iii) $7 - x \le 4 - 2x$

3) Find the ranges of x that satisfy the following inequalities. (And watch that you use the right kind of inequality sign in your answers.)

     a) $3x^2 - 5x - 2 \le 0$,   b) $x^2 + 2x + 7 > 4x + 9$,   c) $3x^2 + 7x + 4 \ge 2\left(x^2 + x - 1\right)$.

4) Find the ranges of x that satisfy these jokers: i) $x^2 + 3x - 1 \ge x + 2$ ii) $2x^2 > x + 1$ iii) $3x^2 - 12 < x^2 - 2x$

5) Solve these sets of simultaneous equations.
     a) $3x - 4y = 7$ and $-2x + 7y = -22$ b) $2x - 3y = \frac{11}{12}$ and $x + y = -\frac{7}{12}$

6) Find where possible (and that's a bit of a clue) the solutions to these sets of simultaneous equations. Interpret your answers geometrically.

     a) $y = x^2 - 7x + 4$ b) $y = 30 - 6x + 2x^2$ c) $x^2 + 2y^2 - 3 = 0$
        $2x - y - 10 = 0$ $y = 2\left(x + 11\right)$ $y = 2x + 4$

7) A bit trickier: find where the following lines meet: a) $y = 3x - 4$ and $y = 7x - 5$,
                                                      b) $y = 13 - 2x$ and $7x - y - 23 = 0$,
                                                      c) $2x - 3y + 4 = 0$ and $x - 2y + 1 = 0$.

Coordinate Geometry

Welcome to geometry club... nice — today I shall be mostly talking about straight lines...

Finding the equation of a line *Through Two Points*

If you get through your exam without having to find the equation of a line through two points, I'm a Dutchman.

EXAMPLE: Find the equation of the line that passes through the points (–3, 10) and (1, 4), and write it in the forms:

$$y - y_1 = m(x - x_1)$$

$$y = mx + c$$

$$ax + by + c = 0$$

— where a, b and c are <u>integers</u>.

You might be asked to write the equation of a line in <u>any</u> of these forms — but they're all similar.
Basically, if you find an equation in one form — you can easily <u>convert</u> it into either of the others.

The *Easiest* to find is y – y₁ = m(x – x₁)...

Point 1 is (–3, 10) and Point 2 is (1, 4)

Label the Points   Label Point 1 as (x_1, y_1) and Point 2 as (x_2, y_2).

Point 1 — $(x_1, y_1) = (-3, 10)$

Point 2 — $(x_2, y_2) = (1, 4)$

It doesn't matter which way round you label them.

Find the Gradient   Find the <u>gradient</u> of the line m — this is $m = \dfrac{y_2 - y_1}{x_2 - x_1}$.

$$m = \frac{4-10}{1-(-3)} = \frac{-6}{4} = -\frac{3}{2}$$

Write Down the Equation   <u>Write down</u> the equation of the line, using the coordinates x_1 and y_1 — this is just $y - y_1 = m(x - x_1)$.

$x_1 = -3$ and $y_1 = 10 \Longrightarrow y - 10 = -\frac{3}{2}(x - (-3))$

$$y - 10 = -\frac{3}{2}(x + 3)$$

...and *Rearrange* this to get the other two forms:

For the form $y = mx + c$, take everything except the y over to the right.

$$y - 10 = -\frac{3}{2}(x + 3)$$

$$\Rightarrow y = -\frac{3}{2}x - \frac{9}{2} + 10$$

$$\Rightarrow y = -\frac{3}{2}x + \frac{11}{2}$$

To find the form $ax + by + c = 0$, take everything over to one side — and then get rid of any fractions.

Multiply the whole equation by 2 to get rid of the 2's on the bottom line.

$$y = -\frac{3}{2}x + \frac{11}{2}$$

$$\Rightarrow \frac{3}{2}x + y - \frac{11}{2} = 0$$

$$\Rightarrow 3x + 2y - 11 = 0$$

Equations of Lines

1) **LABEL** the points (x_1, y_1) and (x_2, y_2).

2) **GRADIENT** — find it and call it m.

3) **WRITE DOWN THE EQUATION** using $y - y_1 = m(x - x_1)$

4) **CONVERT** to one of the other forms, if necessary.

If you end up with an equation like $\frac{3}{2}x - \frac{4}{3}y + 6 = 0$, where you've got a 2 and a 3 on the bottom of the fractions — multiply everything by the <u>lowest common multiple</u> of 2 and 3, i.e. 6.

There ain't nuffink to this geometry lark, Mister...

This is the sort of stuff that looks hard but is actually pretty easy. Finding the equation of a line in that first form really is a piece of cake — the only thing you have to be careful of is when a point has a negative coordinate (or two). In that case, you've just got to make sure you do the subtractions properly when you work out the gradient. See, this stuff ain't so bad...

Coordinate Geometry

More simple stuff for you to have a go at. It's all stuff you've done before, but this time it's used in a different way.

Find the midpoint by Averaging each of the coordinates

Don't complain. It doesn't get any easier than this.

Example: Find the midpoint of AB, where A and B are $(-3, 10)$ and $(1, 4)$ respectively.

Find the <u>midpoint</u> by taking the <u>average</u> of the x- and y-coordinates:
Label the points (x_1, y_1) and (x_2, y_2).

Average x-coordinate $= \dfrac{x_1 + x_2}{2} = \dfrac{-3+1}{2} = -1$

Average y-coordinate $= \dfrac{y_1 + y_2}{2} = \dfrac{10+4}{2} = 7$

These are the midpoint coordinates.

So the midpoint has coordinates $(-1, 7)$

Use Pythagoras to find the Length of a line segment

Example: Find the length of AB, where A and B are $(2, 12)$ and $(6, 7)$ respectively.

Find the <u>length</u> by treating the line segment as the <u>hypotenuse</u> of a right-angled triangle.
Label the points (x_1, y_1) and (x_2, y_2).
Length of side "x" of the triangle $= x_2 - x_1 = 6 - 2 = 4$
Length of side "y" of the triangle $= y_2 - y_1 = 7 - 12 = -5$

So, length of line segment $= \sqrt{(-5)^2 + 4^2} = \sqrt{25 + 16} = \sqrt{41}$

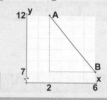

Finding where lines meet means solving Simultaneous Equations

Okay, you can complain now. This is no fun at all.

Two lines... | Line l_1: $5x + 2y - 9 = 0$ or $y = -\frac{5}{2}x + \frac{9}{2}$ | | Line l_2: $3x + 4y - 4 = 0$ or $y = -\frac{3}{4}x + 1$ |

Example: Find where the line l_1 meets the line l_2.

$5x + 2y - 9 = 0$ —①
$3x + 4y - 4 = 0$ —②

Finding where the lines meet means solving these simultaneous equations.

$10x + 4y - 18 = 0$ —③ $= 2 \times$①

$7x - 14 = 0$ —③−②

$\Rightarrow x = 2$

Putting this back into equation ② then gives...

$(3 \times 2) + 4y - 4 = 0$
$\Rightarrow 6 + 4y - 4 = 0$
$\Rightarrow 4y = -2$
$\Rightarrow y = -\frac{1}{2}$

Can't remember how to do simultaneous equations? Have a look at pages 21 & 22.

So the lines meet at the point $\left(2, -\frac{1}{2}\right)$.

If you've got the equations in the form y=mx+c — make the right-hand sides of both equations <u>equal</u>.

Line l_1: $y = -\frac{5}{2}x + \frac{9}{2}$ Line l_2: $y = -\frac{3}{4}x + 1$

$-\frac{5}{2}x + \frac{9}{2} = -\frac{3}{4}x + 1$

Solve this equation to find a value for x.

$\Rightarrow -\frac{7}{4}x = -\frac{7}{2}$

$\Rightarrow x = 2$

Then put this value of x into one of the equations to find the y-coordinate...

$y = -\frac{5}{2} \times 2 + \frac{9}{2}$

It doesn't matter which of the equations you use.

$y = -\frac{1}{2}$

So the lines meet at the point $\left(2, -\frac{1}{2}\right)$.

And I think to myself — what a wonderful page...

What an absolutely superb page. There it is, above all these words that you never read. It's fuller than a student at an all-you-can-eat curry house — absolutely jam- (or madras-) packed with useful things about simultaneous equations, lengths and midpoints. Learn this lot, get a few more marks, get the grades you need, and get yourself into some more all-you-can-eat curry houses.

Coordinate Geometry

This page is based around two really important facts that you've got to know — one about parallel lines, one about perpendicular lines. It's really a page of unparalleled excitement...

Two more lines...

Line l₁
$3x - 4y - 7 = 0$
$y = \frac{3}{4}x - \frac{7}{4}$

Line l₂
$x - 3y - 3 = 0$
$y = \frac{1}{3}x - 1$

...and two points...

Point A $(3, -1)$

Point B $(-2, 4)$

Parallel lines have equal *Gradient*

That's what makes them parallel — the fact that the gradients are the same.

Example: Find the line parallel to l₁ that passes through the point A $(3, -1)$.

Parallel lines have the <u>same gradient</u>.

The original equation is this: $y = \frac{3}{4}x - \frac{7}{4}$

So the new equation will be this: $y = \frac{3}{4}x + c$

We just need to find c.

We know that the line passes through A, so at this point x will be 3, and y will be –1.

Stick these values into the equation to find c.

$$-1 = \frac{3}{4} \times 3 + c$$

$$\Rightarrow c = -1 - \frac{9}{4} = -\frac{13}{4}$$

So the equation of the line is... $y = \frac{3}{4}x - \frac{13}{4}$

And if you're only given the ax + by + c = 0 form it's even easier:

The <u>original</u> line is: $3x - 4y - 7 = 0$

So the <u>new</u> line is: $3x - 4y - k = 0$

Then just use the values of x and y at the point A to find k...

$$3 \times 3 - 4 \times (-1) - k = 0$$

$$\Rightarrow 13 - k = 0$$

$$\Rightarrow k = 13$$

So the equation is: $3x - 4y - 13 = 0$

The gradient of a *Perpendicular* line is: *–1 ÷ the Other Gradient*

Finding <u>perpendicular</u> lines (or '<u>normals</u>') is just as easy as finding parallel lines — as long as you remember the gradient of the perpendicular line is <u>–1 ÷ the gradient of the other one</u>.

Example: Find the line perpendicular to l₂ that passes through the point B $(-2, 4)$.

l₂ has equation: $y = \frac{1}{3}x - 1$

So if the equation of the new line is y=mx+c, then

$$m = -1 \div \frac{1}{3}$$

$$\Rightarrow m = -3$$

Since the gradient of a perpendicular line is: –1 ÷ the other one.

Also... $4 = (-3) \times (-2) + c$

$$\Rightarrow c = 4 - 6 = -2$$

Putting the coordinates of B(–2, 4) into y = mx + c.

So the equation of the line is...

$$y = -3x - 2$$

Or if you start with: l₂ $x - 3y - 3 = 0$

To find a perpendicular line, swap these two numbers around, and change the sign of <u>one of them</u>. (So here, 1 and –3 become 3 and 1.)

So the new line has equation...

$$3x + y + d = 0$$

Or you could have used 3x – y + d = 0.

But... $3 \times (-2) + 4 + d = 0$

$$\Rightarrow d = 2$$

Using the coordinates of point B.

And so the equation of the <u>perpendicular</u> line is...

$$3x + y + 2 = 0$$

Wowzers — parallel lines on the same graph dimension...

This looks more complicated than it actually is, all this tangent and normal business. All you're doing is finding the equation of a straight line through a certain point — the only added complication is that you have to find the gradient first. And there's another way to remember how to find the gradient of a normal — just remember that the gradients of perpendicular lines multiply together to make –1.

Circles

I always say a beautiful shape deserves a beautiful formula, and here you've got one of my favourite double-acts...

Equation of a circle: $(x - a)^2 + (y - b)^2 = r^2$

The equation of a circle looks complicated, but it's all based on Pythagoras' theorem.
Take a look at the circle below, with centre (6, 4) and radius 3.

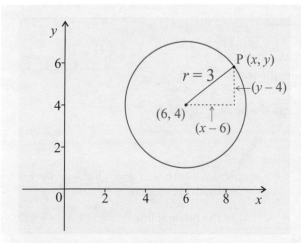

Joining a point P (x, y) on the circumference of the circle to its centre (6, 4), we can create a right-angled triangle.

Now let's see what happens if we use Pythagoras' theorem:

$$(x - 6)^2 + (y - 4)^2 = 3^2$$
or: $(x - 6)^2 + (y - 4)^2 = 9$

This is the equation for the circle. It's as easy as that.

> **In general, a circle with radius r and centre (a, b) has the equation:** $\boxed{(x - a)^2 + (y - b)^2 = r^2}$

Example:

i) What is the centre and radius of the circle with equation $(x - 2)^2 + (y + 3)^2 = 16$

ii) Write down the equation of the circle with centre (–4, 2) and radius 6.

Solution:

i) Comparing $(x - 2)^2 + (y + 3)^2 = 16$ with the general form:

$$(x - a)^2 + (y - b)^2 = r^2$$

then $a = 2$, $b = -3$ and $r = 4$.

> **So the centre (a, b) is: $(2, -3)$**
> **and the radius (r) is: 4.**

And as if by magic, here it is.

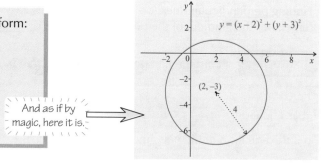

ii) The question says, 'Write down...', so you know you
don't need to do any working.
The centre of the circle is (–4, 2), so $a = -4$ and $b = 2$.
The radius is 6, so $r = 6$.
Using the general equation for a circle $(x - a)^2 + (y - b)^2 = r^2$
you can write: $\boxed{(x + 4)^2 + (y - 2)^2 = 36}$

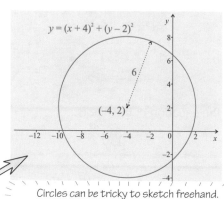

Circles can be tricky to sketch freehand.
A pair of compasses is definitely the way forward.

This is pretty much all you need to learn. Everything on the next page uses stuff you should know already.

Circles

Rearrange the equation into the **familiar form**

Sometimes you'll be given an equation for a circle that doesn't look much like $(x - a)^2 + (y - b)^2 = r^2$.
This is a bit of a pain, because it means you can't immediately tell what the <u>radius</u> is or where the <u>centre</u> is.
But all it takes is a bit of <u>rearranging</u>.

Let's take the equation: $x^2 + y^2 - 6x + 4y + 4 = 0$

You need to get it into the form $(x - a)^2 + (y - b)^2 = r^2$

This is just like completing the square.

Have a look at pages 12-13 for more on completing the square.

$x^2 + y^2 - 6x + 4y + 4 = 0$
$x^2 - 6x + y^2 + 4y + 4 = 0$
$(x - 3)^2 - 9 + (y + 2)^2 - 4 + 4 = 0$
$(x - 3)^2 + (y + 2)^2 = 9$ ⟹ This is the recognisable form, so the centre is **(3, –2)** and the radius is $\sqrt{9}$ = **3**.

Don't forget the Properties of Circles

You will have seen the circle rules at GCSE. You'll sometimes need to dredge them up in your memory for these circle questions. Here's a reminder of a few useful ones.

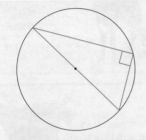

The angle in a semicircle is a right angle.

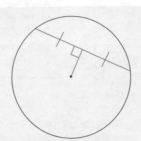

The perpendicular from the centre to a chord bisects the chord.

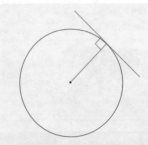

A radius and tangent to the same point will meet at right angles.

Use the Gradient Rule for Perpendicular Lines

Remember that the tangent at a given point will be perpendicular to the radius and the normal at that same point.

Example: Point A (6, 4) lies on a circle with the equation $x^2 + y^2 - 4x - 2y - 20 = 0$.
  i) Find the centre and radius of the circle.
  ii) Find the equation of the tangent to the circle at A.

Solution:

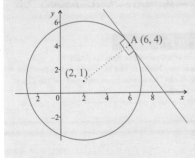

i) Rearrange the equation to show it as the sum of 2 squares:
$x^2 + y^2 - 4x - 2y - 20 = 0$
$x^2 - 4x + y^2 - 2y - 20 = 0$
$(x - 2)^2 - 4 + (y - 1)^2 - 1 - 20 = 0$
$(x - 2)^2 + (y - 1)^2 = 25$
This shows the centre is (2, 1) and the radius is 5.

ii) The tangent is at right angles to the radius at (6, 4).
Gradient of radius at (6, 4) = $\frac{4-1}{6-2} = \frac{3}{4}$
Gradient of tangent = $\frac{-1}{\frac{3}{4}} = -\frac{4}{3}$
Using $y - y_1 = m(x - x_1)$
$y - 4 = -\frac{4}{3}(x - 6)$
$3y - 12 = -4x + 24$
$3y + 4x - 36 = 0$

So the chicken comes from the egg, and the egg comes from the chicken...

Well folks, at least it makes a change from all those straight lines and quadratics.
I reckon if you know the **formula** and **what it means**, you should be absolutely **fine** with questions on circles.

SECTION FOUR — COORDINATE GEOMETRY AND GRAPHS

Cows

The stuff on this page isn't strictly on the syllabus. But I've included it anyway because I reckon it's really important stuff that you ought to know.

There are loads of Different Types of Cows

Dairy Cattle

Every day a dairy cow can produce up to 128 pints of milk — which can be used to make 14 lbs of cheese, 5 gallons of ice cream, or 6 lbs butter.

The Jersey
The Jersey is a small breed best suited to pastures in high rainfall areas. It is kept for its creamy milk.

Advantages
1) Can produce creamy milk until old age.
2) Milk is the highest in fat of any dairy breed (5.2%).
3) Fairly docile, although bulls can't be trusted.

Disadvantages
1) Produces less milk than most other breeds.

The Holstein-Friesian
This breed can be found in many areas. It is kept mainly for milk.

Advantages
1) Produce more milk than any breed.
2) The breed is large, so bulls can be sold for beef.

Disadvantages
1) Milk is low in fat (3.5%).

Beef Cattle

Cows are sedentary animals who spend up to 8 hours a day chewing the cud while standing still or lying down to rest after grazing. Getting fat for people to eat.

The Angus
The Angus is best suited to areas where there is moderately high rainfall.

Advantages
1) Early maturing.
2) High ratio of meat to body weight.
3) Forages well.
4) Adaptable.

The Hereford
The Hereford matures fairly early, but later than most shorthorn breeds. All Herefords have white faces, and if a Hereford is crossbred with any other breed of cow, all the offspring will have white or partially white faces.

Advantages
1) Hardy.
2) Adaptable to different feeds.

Disadvantages
1) Susceptible to eye diseases.

Milk comes from Cows

This is really important — try not to forget it.

Milk is an emulsion of butterfat suspended in a solution of water (roughly 80%), lactose, proteins and salts. Cow's milk has a specific gravity around 1.03.
It's pasteurised by heating it to 63°C for 30 minutes. It's then rapidly cooled and stored below 10°C.

Louis Pasteur began his experiments into 'pasteurisation' in 1856. By 1946, the vacuum pasteurisation method had been perfected, and in 1948, UHT (ultra heat-treated) pasteurisation was introduced.

$$cow + grass = fat\ cow$$
$$fat\ cow + milking\ machine \Rightarrow milk$$

You will often see cows with pieces of grass sticking out of their mouths.

SOME IMPORTANT FACTS TO REMEMBER:
• A newborn calf can walk on its own an hour after birth
• A cow's teeth are only on the bottom of her mouth
• While some cows can live up to 40 years, they generally don't live beyond 20.

Cows on the Internet

For more information on cows, try these websites:

www.allcows.com (including Cow of the Month)
www.crazyforcows.com (with cow e-postcards)
www.moomilk.com (includes a 'What's the cow thinking?' contest.)
http://www.geocities.com/Hollywood/9317/meowcow.html
(for cow-tipping on the Internet)

The Cow
The cow is of the
bovine ilk;
One end is moo,
the other, milk.

— Ogden Nash

Famous Cows and Cow Songs

Famous Cows
1) Ermintrude from the Magic Roundabout.
2) Graham Heifer — the Boddingtons cow.
3) Other TV commercial cows — Anchor, Dairylea
4) The cow that jumped over the moon.
5) Greek Mythology was full of gods turning themselves and their girlfriends into cattle.

Cows in Pop Music
1) Size of a Cow — the Wonder Stuff
2) Saturday Night at the Moo-vies — The Drifters
3) What can I do to make you milk me? — The Cows
4) One to an-udder — the Charlatans
5) Milk me baby, one more time — Britney Spears

Where's me Jersey — I'm Friesian...

Cow-milking — an underrated skill, in my opinion. As Shakespeare once wrote, 'Those who can milk cows are likely to get pretty good grades in maths exams, no word of a lie'. Well, he probably would've written something like that if he was into cows. And he would've written it because cows are helpful when you're trying to work out what a question's all about — and once you know that, you can decide the best way forward. And if you don't believe me, remember the saying of the ancient Roman Emperor Julius Caesar, 'If in doubt, draw a cow'.

Curve Sketching

A picture speaks a thousand words... and graphs are what pass for pictures in maths. They're dead useful in getting your head round tricky questions, and time spent learning how to sketch graphs is time well spent.

Usually, you only need a rough sketch of a graph — so just knowing the basic shapes of these graphs will do.

If you know the Factors of a cubic — the graph's easy to Sketch

A cubic function has an x^3 term in it, and all cubics have 'bottom-left to top-right' shape — or a 'top-left to bottom-right' shape if the coefficient of x^3 is negative.

If you know the factors of a cubic, the graph is easy to sketch — just find where the function is zero.

Example: Sketch the graphs of the following cubic functions.

(i) $f(x) = x(x-1)(2x+1)$

(ii) $g(x) = (1-x)(x^2 - 2x + 2)$

(iii) $h(x) = (x-3)^2(x+1)$

(iv) $m(x) = (2-x)^3$

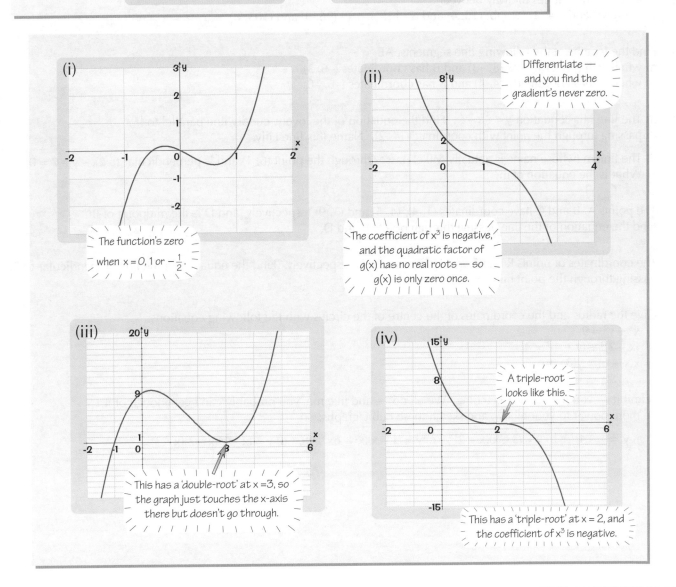

(i) The function's zero when $x = 0, 1$ or $-\frac{1}{2}$.

(ii) Differentiate — and you find the gradient's never zero. The coefficient of x^3 is negative, and the quadratic factor of $g(x)$ has no real roots — so $g(x)$ is only zero once.

(iii) This has a 'double-root' at $x = 3$, so the graph just touches the x-axis there but doesn't go through.

(iv) A triple-root looks like this. This has a 'triple-root' at $x = 2$, and the coefficient of x^3 is negative.

Graphs, graphs, graphs — you can never have too many graphs...

It may seem like a lot to remember, but graphs can really help you get your head round a question — a quick sketch can throw a helluva lot of light on a problem that's got you completely stumped. So being able to draw these graphs won't just help with an actual graph-sketching question — it could help with loads of others too. Got to be worth learning.

Section Four Revision Questions

There you go then... a section on various geometrical things. And in a way it was quite exciting, I'm sure you'll agree. Because it was in this section that the standard and (some might say) slightly dull straight lines and parabolas were joined by the (ever so slightly) more exciting circle. And as you are probably aware, we mathematicians take our excitement from wherever we can get it. That's the good thing about AS maths really — it teaches you to really look hard for excitement at all opportunities, because you know that it's not going to come around too often. Anyway, that's quite enough of me. I'll leave you alone now to savour the lovely questions below to see how much knowledge you've absorbed as a result of working through the section. If you get them all correct, give yourself a pat on the back. If not, read the section again until you know where you went wrong, and try the questions again.

1) Find the equations of the straight lines that pass through the points

    a) $(2, -1)$ and $(-4, -19)$,   b) $(0, -\frac{1}{3})$ and $(5, \frac{2}{3})$.

    Write each of them in the forms

      i) $y - y = m(x - x_1)$ ii) $y = mx + c$ iii) $ax + by + c = 0$, where a, b and c are integers.

2) Find the point that lies midway between:
      a) $(3, -1)$ and $(-4, 3)$ b) $(10, 4)$ and $(2, 11)$ c) $(96, 9)$ and $(103, 8)$

3) Find the lengths of the following line segments, AB:
    a) where A has coordinates $(8, -3)$ and B has coordinates $(-6, 3)$,
    b) where A has coordinates $(4, 4)$ and B has coordinates $(-6, -8)$.

4) a) The line l has equation $y = \frac{3}{2}x - \frac{2}{3}$. Find the equation of the lovely, cuddly line parallel to l,
      passing through the point with coordinates $(4, 2)$. Name this line Lilly.

    b) The line m (whose name is actually Mike) passes through the point $(6, 1)$ and is perpendicular to $2x - y - 7 = 0$.
      What is the equation of m?

5) The points A, B and C have coordinates $(1, 4)$, $(4, 5)$ and $(3, 9)$ respectively, and D is the midpoint of BC. Find the equation of the line passing through points A and D.

6) The coordinates of points R and S are $(1, 10)$ and $(9, 3)$ respectively. Find the equation of the line perpendicular to RS, passing through the point midway between them.

7) Give the radius and the coordinates of the centre of the circles with the following equations:
    a) $x^2 + y^2 = 9$
    b) $(x - 2)^2 + (y + 4)^2 = 4$
    c) $x(x + 6) = y(8 - y)$

8) Admit it — you love curve-sketching. We all do — and like me, you probably can't get enough of it. So more power to your elbow, and sketch these cubic graphs:

    a) $y = (x - 4)^3$,   b) $y = (3 - x)(x + 2)^2$,   c) $y = (1 - x)(x^2 - 6x + 8)$,   d) $y = (x - 1)(x - 2)(x - 3)$.

Differentiation

Brrrrr... differentiation is a bad one — it really is. Not because it's that hard, but because in the exams it comes up all over the place, every time. So if you don't know it perfectly, you're asking for trouble.

Derivative just means 'the thing you get when you differentiate something'.

$$\frac{d}{dx}(x^n) = nx^{n-1}$$

$\frac{d}{dx}$ just means 'the derivative of the thing in the brackets'.

Use this formula to differentiate **Powers of x**

Example: Differentiate y when:

  i) $y = x^5$ ii) $y = 6x^3$ iii) $y = 24x$ iv) $y = 5$

i)
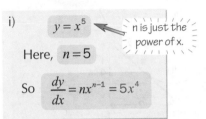
$$y = x^5$$

Here, $n = 5$

So $\frac{dy}{dx} = nx^{n-1} = 5x^4$

n is just the power of x.

ii)
$$y = 6x^3$$

$$\frac{dy}{dx} = 6(3x^2)$$

i.e. $\frac{dy}{dx} = 18x^2$

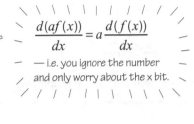

$$\frac{d(af(x))}{dx} = a\frac{d(f(x))}{dx}$$

— i.e. you ignore the number and only worry about the x bit.

iii) $y = 24x$

When you've only got x (which is x¹)...

$$\frac{dy}{dx} = 24(1.x^0)$$

i.e. $\frac{dy}{dx} = 24$

...you just end up with the coefficient of x.

iv) $y = 5$

$\Rightarrow y = 5x^0$

$\Rightarrow \frac{dy}{dx} = 5(0x^{-1}) = 0$

You need every term to be a power of x to differentiate.

Isolated numbers and constants just disappear when you differentiate.

Differentiate each term in an equation **Separately**

This formula is better than cake — even better than that really nice sticky black chocolate one from that place in town. Even if there are loads of terms in the equation, it doesn't matter. Differentiate each bit separately and you'll be fine.

You can do this because: 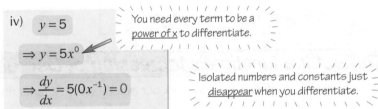 $\dfrac{d(f(x)+g(x))}{dx} = \dfrac{d(f(x))}{dx} + \dfrac{d(g(x))}{dx}$

Example:

Differentiate y when: i) $y = 6x^4 + 4x^3 - 2x + 1$ ii) $y = (x+2)(x+3)$

i) For equations like this...

$$y = 6x^4 + 4x^3 - 2x + 1$$

...just differentiate each term separately.

$$\frac{dy}{dx} = 6(4x^3) + 4(3x^2) - 2 + 0$$

$$\frac{dy}{dx} = 24x^3 + 12x^2 - 2$$

ii) You can't differentiate it until it's written as separate terms which are all powers of x.

$$y = (x+2)(x+3)$$

So multiply out the brackets...

$$y = x^2 + 5x + 6$$

Then it's easy: $\frac{dy}{dx} = 2x + 5$

Dario O'Gradient — differentiating crewe from the rest...

If you're going to bother doing maths, you've got to be able to differentiate things. Simple as that. But luckily, once you can do the simple stuff, you should be all right. Big long equations are just made up of loads of simple little terms, so they're not really that much harder. Learn the rule, and make sure you can use it by practising all day and all night forever.

Differentiation

Differentiation's what you do if you need to find a gradient. Excited yet?

Differentiate to find Gradients

EXAMPLE: Find the gradient of the graph $y = x^2$ at $x = 1$ and $x = -2$...

You need the gradient of the graph of...

$$y = x^2.$$

So differentiate this function to get...

$$\frac{dy}{dx} = 2x.$$

Now when $x = 1$, $\frac{dy}{dx} = 2$.

And so the gradient of the graph at $x = 1$ is 2.

And when $x = -2$, $\frac{dy}{dx} = -4$.

So the gradient of the graph at $x = -2$ is -4.

Use differentiation to find the gradient of a <u>curve</u> — which is the same as the gradient of the <u>tangent</u> at that point.

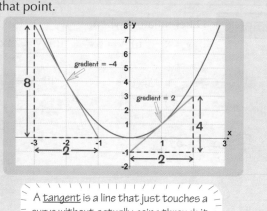

A <u>tangent</u> is a line that just touches a curve without actually going through it.

Find out if a function is Increasing or Decreasing

You can also use differentiation to work out exactly where a function is <u>increasing</u> or <u>decreasing</u> — and how quickly.

A function is <u>increasing</u> when...
...the gradient is <u>positive</u>.

y gets bigger...

...as x gets bigger.

A function is <u>decreasing</u> when...
...the gradient is <u>negative</u>.

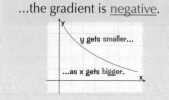

y gets smaller...

...as x gets bigger.

The <u>bigger</u> the gradient...
...the <u>faster</u> y changes with x.

A small change in x means a big change in y.

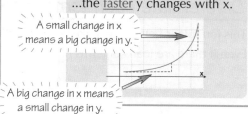

A big change in x means a small change in y.

Example: Find where the following function is <u>increasing</u> and <u>decreasing</u>: $f(x) = 3x^2 - 6x$.

This is a question about <u>gradients</u> — so <u>differentiate</u>.

$$f(x) = 3x^2 - 6x$$
$$\Rightarrow f'(x) = 6x - 6$$

f'(x) pronounced, '<u>f dash of x</u>' (or 'f-prime of x'). is another way to write the derivative.

This is an <u>increasing</u> function when

$$6x - 6 > 0$$
$$\Rightarrow x > 1$$

This is a <u>decreasing</u> function when

$$6x - 6 < 0$$
$$\Rightarrow x < 1$$

Differentiation and Gradients

To find the gradient of a curve at a certain point:

1) **Differentiate the equation** of the curve.

2) **Work out the derivative** at the point.

An increasing function has a <u>positive</u> gradient.

A decreasing function has a <u>negative</u> gradient.

Help me Differentiation — You're my only hope...

There's not much hard maths on this page — but there are a couple of very important ideas that you need to get your head round pretty darn soon. Understanding that differentiating gives the gradient of the graph is more important than washing regularly — AND THAT'S IMPORTANT. The other thing on the page — that you can tell whether a function is getting bigger or smaller by looking at the derivative — is also vital. Sometimes the examiners ask you to find where a function is increasing or decreasing — so you'd just have to find where the derivative was positive or negative.

Differentiation

To find a _stationary point_, you need to find where the graph 'levels off' — that means where the _gradient_ becomes _zero_.

Stationary Points _are when the gradient is_ **Zero**

EXAMPLE: Find the stationary points on the curve $y = 2x^3 - 3x^2 - 12x + 5$, and work out the nature of each one.

A _stationary point_ can be...

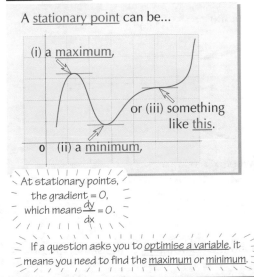

(i) a _maximum_,

or (iii) something like _this_.

0 (ii) a _minimum_,

At stationary points, the gradient = 0, which means $\frac{dy}{dx} = 0$.

If a question asks you to _optimise a variable_, it means you need to find the _maximum_ or _minimum_.

You need to find where $\frac{dy}{dx} = 0$. So first, _differentiate_ the function.

$$y = 2x^3 - 3x^2 - 12x + 5$$
$$\Rightarrow \frac{dy}{dx} = 6x^2 - 6x - 12$$

This is the expression for the gradient.

And then set this derivative equal to _zero_.

$$6x^2 - 6x - 12 = 0$$
$$\Rightarrow x^2 - x - 2 = 0$$
$$\Rightarrow (x - 2)(x + 1) = 0$$
$$\Rightarrow x = 2 \ or \ x = -1$$

See pages 10 to 14 for more about solving quadratics.

So the graph has _two_ stationary points, at $x = 2$ and $x = -1$.

Decide if it's a **Maximum** _or a_ **Minimum** _by differentiating_ **Again**

Once you've found where the stationary points are, you have to decide whether each of them is a _maximum_ or _minimum_ — this is all a question means when it says, '...determine the _nature_ of the turning points'.

To decide whether a stationary point is a _maximum_ or a _minimum_ — just differentiate again to find $\frac{d^2y}{dx^2}$.

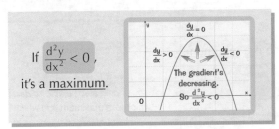

If $\frac{d^2y}{dx^2} < 0$, it's a _maximum_.

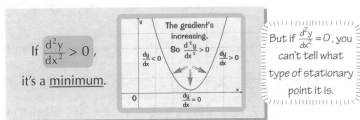

If $\frac{d^2y}{dx^2} > 0$, it's a _minimum_.

But if $\frac{d^2y}{dx^2} = 0$, you can't tell what type of stationary point it is.

You've just found that $\frac{dy}{dx} = 6x^2 - 6x - 12$.

So differentiating again gives $\frac{d^2y}{dx^2} = 12x - 6$.

Stick in the x-coordinates of the stationary points.

At $x = -1$, $\frac{d^2y}{dx^2} = -18$, which is _negative_ — so $x = -1$ is a _maximum_.

And at $x = 2$, $\frac{d^2y}{dx^2} = 18$, which is _positive_ — so $x = 2$ is a _minimum_.

And since a cubic graph (where the coefficient of x^3 is _positive_) goes from _bottom-left to top-right_...

...you can draw a rough sketch of the graph, even though the roots would be hard to find.

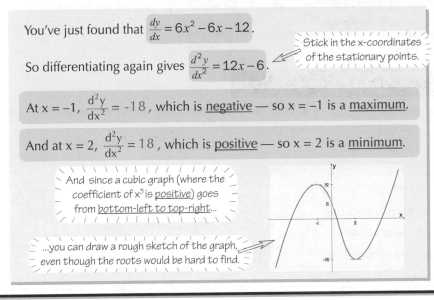

Stationary Points

1) **Find stationary points by solving**
$$\frac{dy}{dx} = 0.$$

2) **Differentiate again to decide whether this is a maximum or a minimum.**

3) **If** $\frac{d^2y}{dx^2} < 0$ — **it's a maximum.**

 If $\frac{d^2y}{dx^2} > 0$ — **it's a minimum.**

An anagram of differentiation is "Perfect Insomnia Cure"...

No joke this, is it — this differentiation business — but it's a dead important topic in maths. It's so important to know how to find whether a stationary point is a max or a min — but it can get a bit confusing. Try remembering MINMAX — which is short for 'MINUS means a MAXIMUM'. Or make up some other clever way to remember what means what.

Curve Sketching

You'll even be asked to do some drawing in the exam... but don't get too excited — it's just drawing graphs... great.

Find where the curve crosses the Axes

Sketch the graph of $f(x) = \frac{x^3}{2} - 3x^2$.

The curve crosses the y-axis when x = 0 — so put x = 0 in the expression for f(x).

When x = 0, f(x) = 0 — so the curve goes through the origin.

Find where the curve crosses the x-axis by solving the equation f(x) = 0.

$$\frac{x^3}{2} - 3x^2 = 0$$
$$\Rightarrow x^3 - 6x^2 = 0$$
$$\Rightarrow x^2(x-6)$$
$$\Rightarrow x = 0 \text{ or } x = 6 \quad \text{So the curve crosses the x-axis when x = 0 and when x = 6.}$$

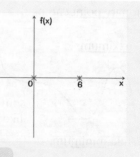

...Differentiate to find Gradient info...

1) Differentiate the function.

$$f(x) = \frac{x^3}{2} - 3x^2$$
$$f'(x) = 3\left(\frac{x^2}{2}\right) - 2(3x^1)$$
$$= \frac{3x^2}{2} - 6x$$

2) So there are stationary points when ...

$$\frac{3x^2}{2} - 6x = 0$$
$$x^2 - 4x = 0$$
$$x(x-4) = 0$$
$$x = 0 \text{ and } x = 4$$

3) Find the coordinates of the stationary points.

At $x = 0$, $f(x) = \frac{(0)^3}{2} - 3(0)^2 = 0$

So there's a stationary point at (0, 0).

At $x = 4$, $f(x) = \frac{(4)^3}{2} - 3(4)^2 = -16$

So there's a stationary point at (4, −16).

4) Differentiate again to see which point is a maximum and which is a minimum.

$$f'(x) = \frac{3x^2}{2} - 6x \Rightarrow f''(x) = 2\left(\frac{3x^1}{2}\right) - 6x^0 = 3x - 6$$

At $x = 0$, $f''(x) = 3(0) - 6 = -6$

$f''(x)$ is negative so (0, 0) is a maximum.

At $x = 4$, $f''(x) = 3(4) - 6 = 6$

$f''(x)$ is positive so (4, −16) is a minimum.

You should also be able to deduce which is a maximum and which is a minimum by considering the general shape of a cubic graph.

...and find out what happens when x gets Big

You can also try and decide what happens as x gets very big — in both the positive and negative directions.

$$f(x) = \frac{x^3}{2} - 3x^2$$

The term with x^3 in it proves the most important term when x gets very big. When x is a big positive number, $\frac{x^3}{2}$ will be a big positive number, and so will f(x). When x is a big negative number, $\frac{x^3}{2}$ will be a big negative number, and so will f(x).

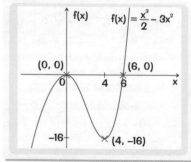

Curve-sketching's important — but don't take my word for it...

Curve-sketching — an underrated skill, in my opinion. As Shakespeare once wrote, 'Those who can do fab sketches of graphs and stuff are likely to get pretty good grades in maths exams, no word of a lie'. And if you don't believe me, remember the saying of the ancient Roman Emperor Julius Caesar, 'If in doubt, draw a graph'.

Section Five Revision Questions

That's what differentiation is all about. And frankly, it probably isn't the worst topic you'll meet in AS maths. Yes, there are fiddly things to remember — but overall, it's not as bad as all that. And just think of all the lovely marks you'll get if you can answer questions like these in the exam...

1) An easy one to start with. Write down the rule for differentiating any power of x.

2) Differentiate these functions with respect to x, and then find the gradients of the graphs at x = 1:

      a) $y = x^2 + 2$,

      b) $y = x^4 + 5x$

      c) $y = 5x(x^2 + 3)$

3) What's the connection between the gradient of a curve at a point and the gradient of the tangent to the curve at the same point? (That sounds like a joke in need of a punchline — but sadly, this is no joke.)

4) Not so easy — it involves inequalities: find when these two functions are increasing and decreasing:

      a) $y = 6(x+2)(x-3)$,

      b) $y = x^3 - 12x$.

5) Write down what a stationary point is. Find the x values which correspond to the stationary points of the graph $y = x(x - 4)(x - 1)$. (Leave your answer in terms of surds.)

6) How can you decide whether a stationary point is a maximum or a minimum?

7) A bit fiddly this — you won't like it — so just make sure you can do it.
Find the stationary points of the function $y = x^3 + 3x^2$.
Decide whether each stationary point is a minimum or a maximum.

8) Now find the stationary points of the function $y = x^3 - 3x$.
Again, decide whether each stationary point is a minimum or a maximum.

Integration

Integration is the 'opposite' of differentiation — and so if you can differentiate, you can be pretty confident you'll be able to integrate too. There's just one extra thing you have to remember — the constant of integration...

You need the constant because there's **More Than One** right answer

When you integrate something, you're trying to find a function that returns to what you started with when you differentiate it. And when you add the constant of integration, you're just allowing for the fact that there's _more_ than one possible function that does this...

This means the Integral of 2x with respect to x.

$$\int 2x\,dx = $$

$$x^2 - 207.253$$
$$x^2 - 1$$
$$x^2$$
$$x^2 + \pi$$

If you differentiate any of these functions, you get the thing on the left — they're _all_ possible answers.

So the answer to this integral is actually...

$$\int 2x\,dx = x^2 + C$$

The '_C_' just means 'any number'. This is the constant of integration.

You only need to add a constant of integration to indefinite integrals — these are just integrals without limits (or little numbers) next to the integral sign. (If that doesn't make sense, you'll see what I mean later on.)

Up the power by **One** — then **Divide** by it

This is an indefinite integral — it doesn't have any limits (numbers) next to the integral sign.

$$\int x^n dx = \frac{x^{n+1}}{n+1} + C$$

In a nutshell, this says:

> To integrate a power of x: (i) Increase the power by one — then divide by it.
>
> and (ii) Stick a constant on the end.

EXAMPLE: Integrate the following with respect to x:
i) x^3 ii) $3x^2 - 2x + 7$ iii) $x^2(x-4)$

$$\int 24x^4 dx = 24\int x^4 dx$$
— i.e. you ignore the number bit in each term and only worry about the x bit. (Just like differentiation.)

i) $$\int x^3 dx = \frac{x^4}{4} + C$$
Increase the power to 4... ...and then divide by 4.

ii) Do each term separately (like with differentiation).

$$\int(3x^2 - 2x + 7)dx$$
$$= \frac{3x^3}{3} - \frac{2x^2}{2} + \frac{7x}{1} + C$$
$$= x^3 - x^2 + 7x + C$$

$$\int(f(x) + g(x))dx = \int f(x)dx + \int g(x)dx$$
— i.e. you can integrate a long expression term by term. (Just like differentiation.)

iii)   Multiply it out first to get separate powers of x terms.

$$\int(x^2(x-4))dx$$
$$= \int(x^3 - 4x^2)dx$$
$$= \frac{x^4}{4} - \frac{4x^3}{3} + C$$

Indefinite integrals — joy without limits...

This integration lark isn't so bad then — there's only a couple of things to remember and then you can do it no problem. But that constant of integration catches loads of people out — it's so easy to forget — and you'll definitely lose marks if you do forget it. You have been warned. Other than that, there's not much to it. Hurray.

Integration

By now, you're probably aware that maths isn't something you do unless you're a bit of a <u>thrill-seeker</u>.
You know, sometimes they even ask you to find a curve with a certain derivative that goes through a certain point.

You sometimes need to find the *Value* of the *Constant of Integration*

When they tell you something else about the curve in addition to its derivative, you can work out the value of that <u>constant of integration</u>. Usually the something is the <u>coordinates</u> of one of the points the curve goes through.

> ### Really Important Bit...
> When you differentiate y, you get $\frac{dy}{dx}$.
> And when you integrate $\frac{dy}{dx}$ you get y. ← If you ignore the constant of integration.
>
> $y \xrightarrow{\text{Differentiate}} \frac{dy}{dx}$
> $y \xleftarrow{\text{Integrate}} \frac{dy}{dx}$

EXAMPLE: Find the equation of the curve through the point (2, 8) with $\frac{dy}{dx} = 6x(x-1)$.

You know the derivative and need to find the function — so <u>integrate</u>.

Remember:
Even if you <u>don't</u> have any extra information about the curve — you still have to add a <u>constant</u> when you work out an integral <u>without limits</u>.

$$\frac{dy}{dx} = 6x(x-1) = 6x^2 - 6x$$

So integrating both sides gives...

$$y = \int (6x^2 - 6x)\,dx$$
$$\Rightarrow y = \frac{6x^3}{3} - \frac{6x^2}{2} + C$$
$$\Rightarrow y = 2x^3 - 3x^2 + C$$

Don't forget the constant of integration.

Check this is correct by differentiating it and making sure you get what you started with.

$$y = 2x^3 - 3x^2 + C = 2x^3 - 3x^2 + Cx^0$$
$$\Rightarrow \frac{dy}{dx} = 2(3x^2) - 3(2x^1) + C(0x^{-1})$$
$$\Rightarrow \frac{dy}{dx} = 6x^2 - 6x$$

So this function's got the correct derivative — but you haven't finished yet.

You now need to <u>find C</u> — and you do this by using the fact that it goes through the point (2, 8).

$$y = 2x^3 - 3x^2 + C$$

Putting x = 2 and y = 8 in the above equation gives...

$$8 = (2 \times 2^3) - (3 \times 2^2) + C$$
$$\Rightarrow 8 = 16 - 12 + C$$
$$\Rightarrow C = 4$$

So the answer you need is this one:

$$y = 2x^3 - 3x^2 + 4$$

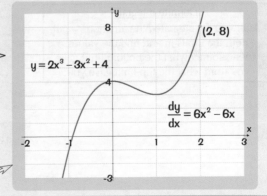

It's a cubic equation — and the graph looks like this...

Maths and alcohol don't mix — so never drink and derive...

That's another page under your belt and — go on, admit it — there was nothing too horrendous on it. If you can do the stuff from the previous page and then substitute some numbers into an equation, you can do everything from this page too. So if you think this is boring, you'd be right. But if you think it's much harder than the stuff before, you'd be wrong.

Integration

Some integrals have <u>limits</u> (i.e. little numbers) next to the integral sign. You integrate in exactly the same way — but you <u>don't</u> need a constant of integration. Much easier. And scrummier and yummier too.

A *Definite Integral* finds the *Area Under a Curve*

The definite integrals below tell you the <u>area</u> between the graph of $y = x^3$ and the x-axis.
The limits (the little numbers at the top and bottom of the integral sign) tell you the extent of the area you're finding.

This marks the right-hand side of the area you're finding.

This marks the left-hand side of the area you're finding.

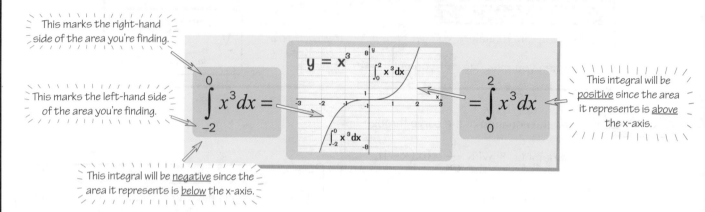

$$\int_{-2}^{0} x^3 \, dx =$$

$y = x^3$

$\int_0^2 x^3 dx$

$\int_{-2}^0 x^3 dx$

$$= \int_0^2 x^3 \, dx$$

This integral will be <u>positive</u> since the area it represents is <u>above</u> the x-axis.

This integral will be <u>negative</u> since the area it represents is <u>below</u> the x-axis.

Do the integration in the same way — then use the *Limits*

Finding a definite integral isn't really any harder than an indefinite one — there's just an <u>extra</u> stage you have to do. After you've integrated the function you have to work out the value of this new function by sticking in the <u>limits</u>.

EXAMPLE:

Evaluate $\int_1^3 \left(x^2 + 2 \right) dx$.

$y = x^2 + 2$

$\int_1^3 (x^2 + 2) dx$

Definite Integrals
After you've integrated the function — put both the limits in and find the values. Then subtract what the bottom limit gave you from what the top limit gave you.

Find the integral in the normal way — then use the limits.

Put the integrated function in <u>square brackets</u> and rewrite the limits on the right-hand side.

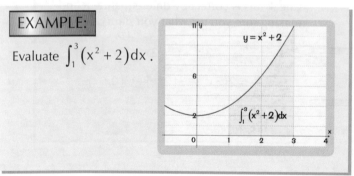

$$\int_1^3 \left(x^2 + 2 \right) dx = \left[\frac{x^3}{3} + 2x \right]_1^3$$

$$= \left(\frac{3^3}{3} + 6 \right) - \left(\frac{1^3}{3} + 2 \right)$$

$$= 15 - \frac{7}{3} = \frac{38}{3}$$

$2 = 2x^0$ — so increase the power (to 1) and divide by 1 to get 2x.

You don't need a constant of integration with a <u>definite</u> integral.

My hobbies? Well I'm really inte grating. Especially carrots.

It's still integration — but this time you're putting two numbers into an equation afterwards. So although this may not be the wild and crazy fun-packed time your teachers promised you when they were trying to persuade you to take AS maths, you've got to admit that a lot of this stuff is pretty similar — and if you can do one bit, you can use that to do quite a few other bits too. Maths is like that. But I admit it's probably not as much fun as a big banana-and-toffee cake.

Section Six Revision Questions

Integration isn't a whole heap different from differentiation really. Well, that's not true — integration is pretty much the *opposite* of differentiation, so in that sense it's completely different. But if you can differentiate, then I'd feel pretty confident that you could integrate as well. Which brings us (kind of) neatly on to these questions. If you've read the section and feel ready to test your integration knowledge, then have a go at the questions below. You need to be aiming to get all of them right. But if you do make a mistake, then it's not the end of the world — just re-read the relevant part of the section and then have another go. And keep doing this until you don't make any mistakes. Then you can feel ready to take on any integration exam questions that Core 1 might throw at you.

1) Write down the steps involved in integrating a power of x.

2) What's an indefinite integral? Why do you have to add a constant of integration when you find an indefinite integral?

3) How can you check whether you've integrated something properly? (Without asking someone else.)

4) Integrate these: a) $\int 10x^4 dx$, b) $\int (3x + 5x^2) dx$, c) $\int (x^2(3x+2)) dx$

5) Work out the equation of the curve that goes through the point (1, 0) and has derivative $\frac{dy}{dx} = 6x - 7$.

6) Find the equation of the curve that has derivative $\frac{dy}{dx} = 3x^3 + 2$ and goes through the point (1, 0). How would you change the equation if the curve had to go through the point (1, 2) instead? (Don't start the whole question again.)

7) How can you tell whether an integral is definite or indefinite? (It's easy really — it just sounds hard.)

8) What does the definite integral $\int_a^b f(x)dx$ represent on a graph?

9) Evaluate: a) $\int_{-3}^{3}(9-x^2)dx$, b) $\int_1^9 \frac{3+x}{4}dx$. Sketch the areas represented by these integrals.

10) Evaluate these definite integrals: a) $\int_0^1 (4x^3 + 3x^2 + 2x + 1)dx$, b) $\int_1^2 (10x^5 + 8x^2)dx$

11) Find the yellow area in each of these graphs:

a)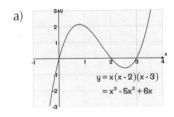

b)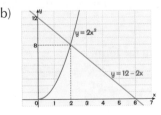

c)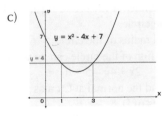

General Certificate of Education
Advanced Subsidiary (AS) and Advanced Level

Core 1 Mathematics — Practice Exam One

You are NOT allowed to use a calculator.

1   A function in x is given by $f(x) = x^2 + mx + 25$, where m is a constant.

    (i)   Find the values of m such that $f(x)$ has no real roots.   [2]

    (ii)   Find the values of m such that $f(x)$ has just one root, and for each of these values of m,
    solve the equation $f(x) = 0$.   [3]

2   The derivative of a function is given by $\dfrac{dy}{dx} = \dfrac{1}{2}(x-6)^2 - 16$

    (i)   Find an expression for y if the graph of y against x is to pass through the point $\left(1, \frac{1}{6}\right)$.   [4]

    (ii)   Evaluate $\displaystyle\int_0^1 y\,dx$.   [4]

3   **(i)**   Sketch the curve $y = (x-2)(x-4)$ and the line $y = 2x - 4$ on the same set of axes, clearly
    marking the coordinates of the points of intersection.   [4]

    (ii)   Evaluate the integral $\displaystyle\int_2^4 (x-2)(x-4)\,dx$.   [3]

    (iii)   Find dy/dx for each of the following:
        (a) $y = x^2$ [1]
        (b) $y = 3x^4 - 2x$ [2]
        (c) $y = (x^2 + 4)(x - 2)$ [2]

4   **(i)**   Either algebraically, or by sketching the graphs, solve the inequality $4x + 7 > 7x + 4$.   [2]

    (ii)   Find the values of k, such that $(x-5)(x-3) > k$ for all possible values of x.   [3]

    (iii)   Find the range of x that satisfies the inequality $(x+3)(x-2) < 2$.   [3]

5   **(i)**   Find the coordinates of the point A, when A lies at the intersection of the lines l_1 and l_2,
    and when the equations of l_1 and l_2 respectively are $x - y + 1 = 0$ and $2x + y - 8 = 0$.   [3]

    (ii)   The points B and C have coordinates $(6, -4)$ and $\left(-\frac{4}{3}, -\frac{1}{3}\right)$ respectively, and D is the midpoint of AC.
    Find the equation of the line BD in the form ax + by + c = 0, where a, b and c are integers.   [5]

    (iii)   Show that the triangle ABD is a right-angled triangle.   [3]

6   The diagram shows a circle. A (2, 1) and B (0, –5) lie on the circle and AB is a diameter.
    C (4, –1) is also on the circle.
    (i)   Find the centre and radius of the circle.   [4]
    (ii)   Show that the equation of the circle can be written in the form:
        $x^2 + y^2 - 2x + 4y - 5 = 0$ [3]
    (iii)   The tangent at A and the normal at C cross at D.
    Find the coordinates of D.   [8]

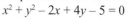

7   A curve has equation $y = f(x)$, where dy/dx = $4(1 - x)$.
    The curve passes through the point A, with coordinates (2, 6).
    (i)   Find the equation of the curve.   [4]
    (ii)   Sketch the graph of $y = f(x)$.   [3]
    (iii)   Find the equation of the normal to the curve at A.   [2]

8   A curve that passes through the point (2, 0) has derivative $\dfrac{dy}{dx} = 3x^2 + 6x - 4$.

    (i)   Show that the equation of the curve is $y = x^3 + 3x^2 - 4x - 12$.   [3]
    (ii)   Show that $(x + 3)$ is a factor of y.   [2]
    (iii)   Express y as a product of 3 linear factors.   [2]

Paper 1 Q1 — Quadratics

1 A function in x is given by $f(x) = x^2 + mx + 25$, where m is a constant.

(i) Find the values of m such that $f(x)$ has no real roots. **[2]**

(ii) Find the values of m such that $f(x)$ has just one root, and for each of these values of m, solve the equation $f(x) = 0$. **[3]**

(i) | Use the Discriminant

'Find the values of m such that $f(x)$ has no real roots.'

1) When a question starts mentioning the **number of roots** of a quadratic, you're bound to need the **discriminant**.

2) There's more about this on page 13, but in short it's 'the bit in the square root' from the quadratic formula: $b^2 - 4ac$

3) Negative numbers don't have real square roots — so to get no real roots you want $b^2 - 4ac < 0$.

For this question, you've got: $a = 1$, $b = m$ and $c = 25$

So for $b^2 - 4ac < 0$, you get:
$m^2 - 4 \times 1 \times 25 < 0$
$m^2 - 100 < 0$
$m^2 < 100$
$-10 < m < 10$

You might like to tackle this by visualising a graph of $y = x^2 - 100$. When $y < 0$ (i.e. when the graph is below the x-axis), x lies between −10 and 10.

(ii) | Guess what — Use the Discriminant again...

'Find the values of m such that $f(x)$ has just one root...'

For just one root, you need the discriminant = 0:
$b^2 - 4ac = 0$
$m^2 - 100 = 0$
$m^2 = 100$
$m = \pm 10$

'for each of these values of m, solve the equation $f(x) = 0$.'

This is the easy(ish) bit — just substitute for m and factorise.

If $m = 10$, you've got: $x^2 + 10x + 25 = 0$
this will factorise: $(x + 5)(x + 5) = 0$
$x = -5$

For $m = -10$, it's almost the same: $x^2 - 10x + 25 = 0$
$(x - 5)(x - 5) = 0$
$x = 5$

In fact they're both perfect squares, which you could've predicted, since you're after a single root.

Ladies and Gentlemen — repeat after me...

Discriminant > 0 gives **2 real roots**
Discriminant = 0 gives **1 real root**
Discriminant < 0 gives **0 real roots**
Got it... good.

Paper 1 Q2 — Calculus

2 The derivative of a function is given by $\frac{dy}{dx} = \frac{1}{2}(x-6)^2 - 16$

   (i) Find an expression for y if the graph of y against x is to pass through the point $\left(1, \frac{1}{6}\right)$.   **[4]**

   (ii) Evaluate $\int_0^1 y\,dx$.   **[4]**

(i) You just *Integrate* it...

'Find an expression for y if the graph of y against x is to pass through the point $\left(1, \frac{1}{6}\right)$.'

To get an expression for y from an expression for $\frac{dy}{dx}$, you just <u>integrate</u>.

(Integration is the opposite of differentiation, remember.)

Before you can integrate it, you have to rewrite $\frac{dy}{dx}$ as 'de-simplified' <u>powers of x</u>...

$$\frac{dy}{dx} = \frac{1}{2}(x-6)^2 - 16$$
$$= \frac{1}{2}\{x^2 - 12x + 36\} - 16$$
$$= \frac{1}{2}x^2 - 6x + 2$$

Expand the brackets to get separate coefficients for separate powers of x.

Now write both sides as integrals...

Just put an integral sign and 'dx' around both sides for now.

$$\int \frac{dy}{dx}dx = \int\left(\frac{1}{2}x^2 - 6x + 2\right)dx$$

Integrate the left-hand side and you get y. Integrate the right-hand side, and you get...

$$y = \frac{x^3}{6} - 3x^2 + 2x + C$$

Integrating $\frac{dy}{dx}$ gives y.

Don't forget that constant of integration.

If you wanted to practise, or you had a really difficult expression to integrate, don't forget — you could have split up the integral into 3 separate bits:

The integration formula:

$$\int x^n dx = \frac{x^{n+1}}{n+1} + C$$

Integrate each term separately...

$$y = \frac{1}{2}\int x^2 dx - 6\int x\,dx + \int 2\,dx$$

Don't forget the signs (+'s and –'s). I'm just showing the actual integrals — not their mathematical persuasion!

$$\frac{1}{2}\left(\frac{x^3}{3}\right) \quad 6\left(\frac{x^2}{2}\right) \quad 2x$$

Get the signs right.

$$y = \frac{x^3}{6} - 3x^2 + 2x + C$$

...and add a <u>constant of integration</u>.

You always have to stick in a constant of integration — you don't know what it is yet, so call it C for now.

You might wonder why there's only one constant. Since you've had to do four separate mini-integrations, shouldn't there be four constants like this?

$$y + C_1 = \frac{x^3}{6} + C_2 - 3x^2 + C_3 + 2x + C_4$$

Well yes, but rather than have four separate ones, you can just make them into one.

Let $C = -C_1 + C_2 + C_3 + C_4 \Rightarrow y = \frac{x^3}{6} - 3x^2 + 2x + C$

Paper 1 Q2 — Calculus

'...to pass through the point $\left(1, \frac{1}{6}\right)$.'

To make sure the curve goes through the right point, you have to find the correct value for C.

To do this, stick in the values $x = 1$ and $y = \frac{1}{6}$, and the value of C will just pop out.

Substitute $x = 1$ and $y = \frac{1}{6}$ in the expression for y...

$$y = \frac{x^3}{6} - 3x^2 + 2x + C$$

$$\Rightarrow \frac{1}{6} = \frac{1^3}{6} - \left(3 \times 1^2\right) + \left(2 \times 1\right) + C$$

$$\Rightarrow \frac{1}{6} = \frac{1}{6} - 1 + C$$

$$\Rightarrow C = 1$$

And so the complete expression for y is...

$$y = \frac{x^3}{6} - 3x^2 + 2x + 1$$

(ii) A simple **Limit Integral** — but don't fall into the **Trap**

'Evaluate $\int_0^1 y\,dx$.' This part is pretty standard stuff — but there's a really obvious trap at the start. As long as you avoid that, you can't go far wrong.

You need to find $\int_0^1 y\,dx$.

Now the '<u>dx</u>' means you're integrating <u>with respect to x</u>. So you need to write y <u>in terms of x</u> before you integrate. But that's what you've just found — so stick in your answer to part (i).

The Trap:

$$\int_0^1 y\,dx = \left[\frac{y^2}{2}\right]_0^1 = \frac{1}{2} - 0 = \frac{1}{2}$$

This answer's <u>rubbish</u>! It's integrating with respect to y, when it should be x.

$$\int_0^1 y\,dx = \int_0^1 \left(\frac{x^3}{6} - 3x^2 + 2x + 1\right)dx$$

You could break this up into individual chunks like before — but you don't have to. Do whatever's easier.

It's a limit integral, so integrate the bracket — and stick it in a big square bracket with limits.

$$\int_0^1 y\,dx = \int_0^1 \left(\frac{x^3}{6} - 3x^2 + 2x + 1\right)dx = \left[\frac{x^4}{6 \times 4} - \frac{3x^3}{3} + \frac{2x^2}{2} + \frac{1x^1}{1}\right]_0^1$$

$$= \left[\frac{x^4}{24} - x^3 + x^2 + x\right]_0^1$$

Now evaluate the square bracket — use the <u>top limit</u> first, then <u>subtract</u> what you get when you use the <u>bottom limit</u>.

$$\int_0^1 y\,dx = \left(\frac{1^4}{24} - 1^3 + 1^2 + 1\right) - \left(\frac{0^4}{24} - 0^3 + 0^2 + 0\right)$$

When you put x = 0, all these parts are equal to zero.

$$= \frac{1}{24} - 1 + 1 + 1$$

$$= \frac{25}{24}$$

Integration — I'n't it great? ...no? Oh... didn't think so...

This question is a gift — it's all real standard stuff. So if you're struggling with it, bury your head in those maths books until it begins to make sense. And another thing — always make sure you use all the info the question gives you, e.g. if it says the graph passes through the point (joe, bloggs), it means "at some point in the question, you need to plug in the values x=joe when y=bloggs". And watch for that trap at the end — the 'dx' in an integral means you have to integrate x's.

Paper 1 Q3 — Integration and Differentiation

3 **(i)** Sketch the curve $y = (x-2)(x-4)$ and the line $y = 2x-4$ on the same set of axes, clearly
   marking the coordinates of the points of intersection. [4]

   (ii) Evaluate the integral $\int_2^4 (x-2)(x-4)\,dx$. [3]

   (iii) Find dy/dx for each of the following:
       (a) $y = x^2$ [1]
       (b) $y = 3x^4 - 2x$ [2]
       (c) $y = (x^2+4)(x-2)$ [2]

(i) Solve some *Simultaneous Equations* and Sketch a *Curve*

'Sketch the curve $y = (x-2)(x-4)$ and the line $y = 2x-4$ ...'

The question says you have to mark in the coordinates of the points where the parabola and the straight line cross.
It's probably a good idea to find these <u>before</u> you draw anything — and that means solving simultaneous equations.

So solve these simultaneous equations to find the intersection points.

$$y = (x-2)(x-4) \quad \text{①}$$
$$y = 2x-4 \quad \text{②}$$

It's best to label them first.

Simultaneous equations where one of them is quadratic — straight away, think <u>substitution</u>. So...

A Substitute y from equation 2 into equation 1:

$$2x-4 = (x-2)(x-4)$$
$$\Rightarrow 2x-4 = x^2 - 6x + 8$$

Rearrange things so that everything is on one side and you get...

$$x^2 - 8x + 12 = 0$$
$$\Rightarrow (x-2)(x-6) = 0$$
$$\Rightarrow x = 2 \quad or \quad x = 6$$

These are the x-coordinates of the points of intersection.

Now find the y-coordinates:

$$x = 2 \quad \text{in equation } 2 \Rightarrow y = (2 \times 2) - 4 = 0$$

$$x = 6 \quad \text{in equation } 2 \Rightarrow y = (2 \times 6) - 4 = 8$$

So the two points of intersection are: $(2, 0)$ and $(6, 8)$.

B Then drawing the graph is easy. The parabola
crosses the x-axis at x = 2 and x = 4, and it
crosses the line at x = 2 and x = 6.

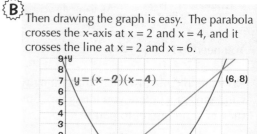

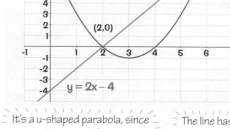

It's a u-shaped parabola, since the coefficient of x² is positive.
The line has gradient 2.

(ii) A pretty easy *Integration*

'Evaluate the integral $\int_2^4 (x-2)(x-4)\,dx$.'

A pretty standard integration — shouldn't cause too many problems really...

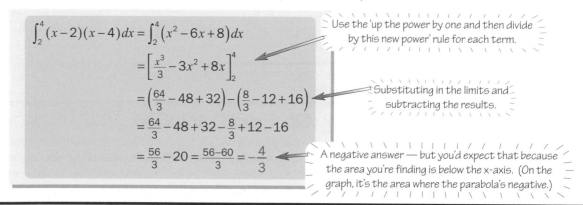

$$\int_2^4 (x-2)(x-4)\,dx = \int_2^4 (x^2 - 6x + 8)\,dx$$

$$= \left[\frac{x^3}{3} - 3x^2 + 8x \right]_2^4$$

$$= \left(\frac{64}{3} - 48 + 32 \right) - \left(\frac{8}{3} - 12 + 16 \right)$$

$$= \frac{64}{3} - 48 + 32 - \frac{8}{3} + 12 - 16$$

$$= \frac{56}{3} - 20 = \frac{56-60}{3} = -\frac{4}{3}$$

Use the 'up the power by one and then divide by this new power' rule for each term.

Substituting in the limits and subtracting the results.

A negative answer — but you'd expect that because the area you're finding is below the x-axis. (On the graph, it's the area where the parabola's negative.)

Paper 1 Q3 — Integration and Differentiation

(iii) Just use the Rule for Differentiation

'Find dy/dx for each of the following:'

(a) $y = x^2$.

When you need to find dy/dx or $f'(x)$, it means you need to **differentiate**.

$$y = x^2$$
$$\frac{dy}{dx} = 2x^1$$
$$= \boxed{2x}$$

x^1 is just x.

If you've forgotten the rule for differentiating powers of x, flick back to page 35.

(b) $y = 3x^4 - 2x$.

Again you can use the rule for differentiation — but there are two terms, so you do it twice.

For the first term $n = 4$, and for the second term $n = 1$:

$$y = 3x^4 - 2x$$
$$\frac{dy}{dx} = 3(4x^{4-1}) - 2(1x^{1-1})$$
$$= 3(4x^3) - 2(1)$$
$$= \boxed{12x^3 - 2}$$

Don't let the coefficients in front of the x bits put you off — you just multiply by them. In maths-speak, that's $\frac{d}{dx}(ky) = k\frac{dy}{dx}$.

(c) $y = (x^2 + 4)(x - 2)$.

When you need to differentiate an expression like this, you have to multiply it out first.

$$y = (x^2 + 4)(x - 2)$$
$$y = x^3 - 2x^2 + 4x - 8$$

This gives you a set of terms which are all powers of x. Which makes everything lovely.
Now differentiate each term:

$$y = x^3 - 2x^2 + 4x - 8$$
$$\frac{dy}{dx} = 3x^{3-1} - 2(2x^{2-1}) + 4(1x^{1-1}) - 0$$
$$= \boxed{3x^2 - 4x + 4}$$

Constant terms always disappear when you differentiate. That's because for a constant, the power of x is 0, so when you differentiate, you end up multiplying the term by 0, which gives 0. Glad we've cleared that up...

It'd be great if the summer term disappeared...

...and the spring one and the autumn one. Differentiation strikes fear into the hearts of the hardest of maths students.
It can get a little sticky at times, so make sure you know the rules really well.
Even then you probably won't be laughing, but at least you might be slightly more optimistic.

Paper 1 Q4 — Inequalities...

4 (i) Either algebraically, or by sketching the graphs, solve the inequality $4x + 7 > 7x + 4$. [2]

(ii) Find the values of k, such that $(x-5)(x-3) > k$ for all possible values of x. [3]

(iii) Find the range of x that satisfies the inequality $(x+3)(x-2) < 2$. [3]

(i) A straightforward **Linear Inequality**

'Either algebraically, or by sketching the graphs...'

That opening makes it sound really tricky, but don't be fooled. Sketching graphs sounds much easier, but it's such a <u>simple</u> inequality that it's much quicker to just work it out:

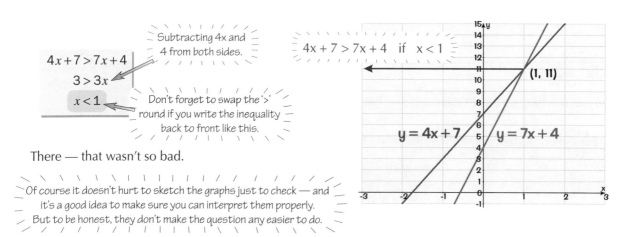

Subtracting 4x and 4 from both sides.

$$4x + 7 > 7x + 4$$
$$3 > 3x$$
$$x < 1$$

$4x + 7 > 7x + 4$ if $x < 1$

Don't forget to swap the '>' round if you write the inequality back to front like this.

There — that wasn't so bad.

Of course it doesn't hurt to sketch the graphs just to check — and it's a good idea to make sure you can interpret them properly. But to be honest, they don't make the question any easier to do.

(ii) Easy — if you spot the **Symmetry**

'Find the values of k, such that $(x-5)(x-3) > k$ for all possible values of x.'

Basically, you've got to find the <u>minimum</u> value of $(x-5)(x-3)$, and make sure k is less than that.

Another way you could to this part would be to multiply out the brackets and complete the square.

As always, if you're a bit unsure where to start, think what the function looks like — and <u>SKETCH THE GRAPH</u>.

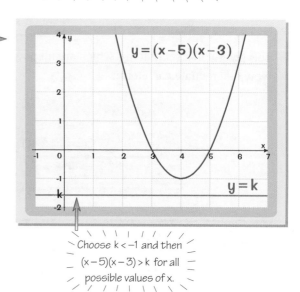

Here's the cunning bit: The thing to realise is that the graph's <u>symmetrical</u> — so the minimum will be halfway between x = 3 and x = 5 — i.e. x = 4. So just plug that into the equation to find the lowest point the graph reaches:

Putting x = 4 in (x − 5)(x − 3) gives

$$(4-5)(4-3) = -1 \times 1$$
$$= -1$$

So if $k < -1$, the graph will never be as low as k.

Choose k < −1 and then $(x-5)(x-3) > k$ for all possible values of x.

Paper 1 Q4 — ...and Quadratics

(iii) Draw the **Graph** to see when it's **Negative**

'Find the range of x that satisfies the inequality $(x+3)(x-2) < 2$.'

You need to find a 'range of x' — not just one value. Sounds a bit complicated — but it's not too bad once you get going. The first thing to do is rearrange the equation so you've got <u>zero</u> on one side.

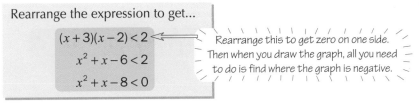

Rearrange the expression to get...

$$(x+3)(x-2) < 2$$
$$x^2 + x - 6 < 2$$
$$x^2 + x - 8 < 0$$

Rearrange this to get zero on one side. Then when you draw the graph, all you need to do is find where the graph is negative.

Then sketch the graph of $y = x^2 + x - 8$. And since you're interested in when this is less than zero, make sure you find out where this crosses the <u>x-axis</u>.

When the graph crosses the x-axis, it changes from positive to negative, or vice versa.

Now $x^2 + x - 8$ doesn't factorise — so find out where it crosses the x-axis by using the <u>quadratic formula</u>.

You can tell it doesn't factorise because $\sqrt{b^2 - 4ac} = \sqrt{33}$ — and that's not a whole number or an 'easy' decimal.

Now, $x^2 + x - 8 = 0$ when

$$x = \frac{-1 \pm \sqrt{1^2 - (4 \times 1 \times -8)}}{2 \times 1}$$
$$= \frac{-1 \pm \sqrt{33}}{2}$$

The quadratic formula:
$$x = \frac{-b \pm \sqrt{b^2 - 4ac}}{2a}$$
when
$$ax^2 + bx + c = 0$$

So the graph looks like this:

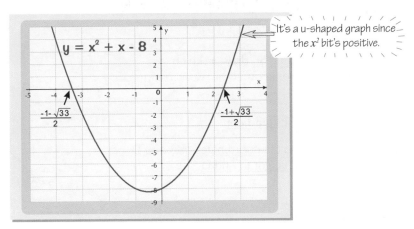

It's a u-shaped graph since the x^2 bit's positive.

And since you need this to be <u>negative</u> — it's pretty clear that the range of x you're interested in is...

$$\frac{-1-\sqrt{33}}{2} < x < \frac{-1+\sqrt{33}}{2}$$

$a < x < b$ means 'x between a and b'.

It's easy to check — just stick the two numbers back into the original inequality and make sure the left-hand side equals 2.

These can be pretty darn hard unless you draw the graphs...

It's true. These questions can be very hard unless you have a picture to look at. It just helps you understand exactly what's going on, and what the examiners are going on about. That's the thing with these questions — they can look so intimidating. But drawing a picture helps you get your head round it — and once you've got your head round it, it's much easier to work towards the answer. Mmmm... I think I've said enough on that for now.

PRACTICE EXAM ONE

Paper 1 Q5 — Geometry

5 (i) Find the coordinates of the point A, when A lies at the intersection of the lines l_1 and l_2, and when the equations of l_1 and l_2 respectively are

$$x - y + 1 = 0 \quad \text{and} \quad 2x + y - 8 = 0.$$

[3]

(ii) The points B and C have coordinates $(6, -4)$ and $\left(-\frac{4}{3}, -\frac{1}{3}\right)$ respectively, and D is the midpoint of AC.

Find the equation of the line BD in the form $ax + by + c = 0$, where a, b and c are integers. [5]

(iii) Show that the triangle ABD is a right-angled triangle. [3]

(i) Finding A is easy — it's just Simultaneous Equations...

'Find the coordinates of the point A...'

A is the point where these two lines intersect. So to find its coordinates, you need to solve the two lines as a pair of <u>simultaneous equations</u>.

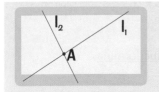

Line 1 — ①— $x - y + 1 = 0$

Line 2 — ②— $2x + y - 8 = 0$

Get rid of y to find x:

①+② $\quad (x + 2x) + (-y + y) + (1 - 8) = 0$

$$3x - 7 = 0$$

$$x = \tfrac{7}{3}$$

Stick x=7/3 back into l_1 to find y:

① $\quad x - y + 1 = 0$

$$\tfrac{7}{3} - y + 1 = 0$$

$$y = \tfrac{7}{3} + 1 = \tfrac{10}{3}$$

So A is $\left(\tfrac{7}{3}, \tfrac{10}{3}\right)$

Forgotten everything you ever knew about simultaneous equations? Have a look at page 20.

(ii) Equation of a line — find the Gradient First...

'Find the equation of the line BD in the form ax + by + c = 0...'

This question gives you loads of information. So draw a sketch. Otherwise you won't have a clue what's going on. (Well I wouldn't anyway.)

To find the equation of a line, you'll need its <u>gradient</u>.

And to find the gradient of BD, you'll need the <u>coordinates</u> of B and D — you're given B in the question, but <u>you've got to find D</u>.

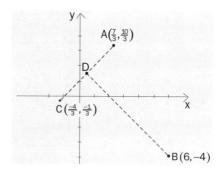

Find D (the midpoint of A and C)

You get the midpoint of two points by finding the <u>average</u> of the x-coordinates, and the <u>average</u> of the y-coordinates.

Midpoint of AC is... $\left(\dfrac{x_A + x_C}{2}, \dfrac{y_A + y_C}{2}\right)$

x_A is the x-coordinate of the point A. y_C is the y-coordinate of the point C.

which is... $= \left(\dfrac{\tfrac{7}{3} + \tfrac{-4}{3}}{2}, \dfrac{\tfrac{10}{3} + \tfrac{-1}{3}}{2}\right) = \left(\tfrac{1}{2}, \tfrac{3}{2}\right)$

So D is... $\left(\tfrac{1}{2}, \tfrac{3}{2}\right)$

Find the Gradient of BD

$$\text{Gradient} = \frac{\text{difference in y-coordinates}}{\text{difference in x-coordinates}}$$

m_{BD} is the gradient of the line BD.

$$m_{BD} = \frac{y_D - y_B}{x_D - x_B} = \frac{\tfrac{3}{2} - -4}{\tfrac{1}{2} - 6} = \frac{3 + 8}{1 - 12} = -1$$

Paper 1 Q5 — Geometry

So you've got the gradient... Well now you can do anything — you can sail around the world, you can become the richest person in the world, you can rule the world... you can become more powerful than you can possibly imagine...

Find the Equation of BD

I reckon y=mx+c is the nicest form for the equation of a straight line. So I'd get it in that form first.

$$y = m_{BD}x + c \Rightarrow y = -x + c$$

The equation will be like this because we've just worked out that the gradient is –1 — you just need to find what c is.

Putting in the values for x and y at <u>either</u> point B <u>or</u> point D will give you the value of c.

At point B, x=6 and y=-4

$$y = mx + c$$
$$-4 = -6 + c$$
$$c = 2$$

y=mx+c is great — m is the gradient, and c is where the line crosses the y-axis.

So equation for BD is: $y = -x + 2$

$$x + y - 2 = 0$$

Make sure it's in the form the question asks for.

(iii) | **Right-angled triangle? Check if the lines are Perpendicular**

'Show that the triangle ABD is a right-angled triangle.'

The first thing to do is update your sketch (or do a new one) with the triangle ABD on.

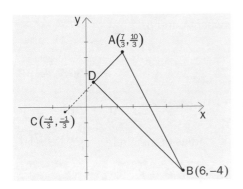

You've got to show that ABD is right-angled. To do this, just show that two sides of the triangle are <u>perpendicular</u> to each other (so their gradients multiply to give –1).

(That means you'll have a right angle in the corner where the sides meet.)

See page 26 for more info on perpendicular lines.

Show that the gradients of AD and BD multiply together to give –1:

Gradient of AD: $m_{DA} = \dfrac{y_D - y_A}{x_D - x_A} = \dfrac{\frac{3}{2} - \frac{10}{3}}{\frac{1}{2} - \frac{7}{3}} = \dfrac{9 - 20}{3 - 14} = 1$

Gradients of perpendicular lines multiply together to make –1.

And you already know the gradient of BD is: $m_{BD} = -1$

So... $m_{BD} \times m_{DA} = -1 \times 1 = -1$

So angle ADB is a <u>right-angle</u>. Fantastic.

Look how happy maths can make you... I bet you're jumping for joy too...

So you've proved it's a right-angled triangle and completed a stinker of a question. Now you can...

...become the Master of the Universe...

To avoid getting into trouble while you're doing this question, you've got to draw what's happening before you do each part. So when you read stuff like "The points B and C have coordinates (6,–4) and..." you should dive for your pencil and sketch all the information it gives you. And then <u>use</u> the sketch and <u>plan</u> how you're going to answer the question.

Paper 1 Q6 — Circles

6   The diagram shows a circle. A (2, 1) and B (0, –5) lie on the circle and AB is a diameter.
     C (4, –1) is also on the circle.

   (i)   Find the centre and radius of the circle.   [4]

   (ii) Show that the equation of the circle can be written in the form:
         $$x^2 + y^2 - 2x + 4y - 5 = 0$$ [3]

   (iii) The tangent at A and the normal at C cross at D.
         Find the coordinates of D.   [8]

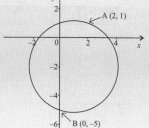

(i) | *Average the Coordinates, then do a bit of Pythagoras*

'Find the centre and radius of the circle.'

The centre of the circle must be at the midpoint of AB, since AB is a diameter.

To get the midpoint, you **average the x- and y-coordinates**.

Midpoint of AB is: $\left(\dfrac{2+0}{2}, \dfrac{1+-5}{2}\right) = (1, -2)$

As AB is the diameter, the length of the radius will be half the distance between A and B.

You can use Pythagoras' theorem to find the distance.
A quick sketch usually helps with these:

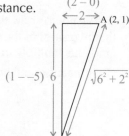

If you've forgotten about surds, see p 2.

$$AB = \sqrt{40} = 2\sqrt{10}$$
$$\text{Radius of the circle} = \frac{1}{2}AB = \sqrt{10}$$

(ii) | *Use the General Equation of a Circle*

'Show that the equation of the circle can be written in the form: $x^2 + y^2 - 2x + 4y - 5 = 0$'

The general equation for a circle with centre (a, b) and radius r is: $(x - a)^2 + (y - b)^2 = r^2$

For this circle you have: $a = 1, \ b = -2, \ r = \sqrt{10}$
$$(x - 1)^2 + (y + 2)^2 = 10$$

If we multiply out the brackets, you should be able to get the form given in the question:

$$(x - 1)(x - 1) + (y + 2)(y + 2) = 10$$
$$x^2 - 2x + 1 + y^2 + 4y + 4 = 10$$
$$x^2 + y^2 - 2x + 4y - 5 = 0$$

Paper 1 Q6 — Circles

(iii) *Tangents **touch** circles, Normals are at **right angles** to them*

'Find the coordinates of D.'

A little bit of sketching on the diagram provided is always a good idea.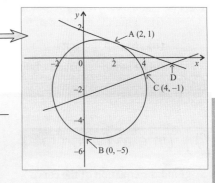

You need to find the equations of the tangent and normal and then work out where they cross.

The tangent at A: This is at right angles to the radius and diameter at A — you can use this to find the gradient.

The gradient of a line joining (x_1, y_1) to (x_2, y_2) is given by: $\dfrac{y_2 - y_1}{x_2 - x_1}$

For AB, gradient = $\dfrac{1--5}{2-0} = \dfrac{6}{2} = 3$

Use $y - y_1 = m(x - x_1)$ to get the equation of the tangent.

$m = -\dfrac{1}{3}$, (x_1, y_1) is the point (2, 1)

The **tangent is perpendicular to the diameter**, so use the gradient rule to find the gradient of the tangent.

$\dfrac{-1}{\text{gradient of AB}} = -\dfrac{1}{3}$

See p 27 if you've forgotten the gradient rule.

$y - 1 = -\dfrac{1}{3}(x - 2)$

$y - 1 = -\dfrac{1}{3}x + \dfrac{2}{3}$

$y = -\dfrac{1}{3}x + \dfrac{5}{3}$

So that's your equation for the tangent of the circle at point A.

The normal at C: A normal passes through the centre, so its gradient is the gradient from the centre to C.

You can use: $y - y_1 = m(x - x_1)$ to get the equation of the normal.

Gradient = $\dfrac{-1--2}{4-1} = \dfrac{1}{3}$

Where $m = \dfrac{1}{3}$, (x_1, y_1) is the point (4, -1).

$y--1 = \dfrac{1}{3}(x - 4)$

$y + 1 = \dfrac{1}{3}x - \dfrac{4}{3}$

$y = \dfrac{1}{3}x - \dfrac{7}{3}$

So here's your equation for the normal at point C.

Where they cross: To get the coordinates of D, you need to find where the lines cross.

Put the equations equal to each other and solve:

$-\dfrac{1}{3}x + \dfrac{5}{3} = \dfrac{1}{3}x - \dfrac{7}{3}$

$\dfrac{5}{3} + \dfrac{7}{3} = \dfrac{1}{3}x + \dfrac{1}{3}x$

$4 = \dfrac{2}{3}x$

$x = 6$

Put this back into one of the equations to get y:

$y = -\dfrac{1}{3}x + \dfrac{5}{3}$

$y = -\dfrac{1}{3} \times 6 + \dfrac{5}{3}$

$y = -2 + \dfrac{5}{3}$

$y = -\dfrac{1}{3}$

So... D has coordinates $(6, -\dfrac{1}{3})$

Circles — a great shape for wheels...

OK, so at first glance this *looks* like a dirty great big question on circles. In fact, it's only half a dirty great big question on circles and half a dirty great big question on graphs. Tangents and normals questions are pretty much the same, whatever the shape of the curve you're looking at. All you need is the equation of the line and you're away. And if you notice, they give you the equation of the line in part (ii) — so you can still do part (iii), even if you make a pig's ear of the first two bits.

Paper 1 Q7 — Integration and Graphs

7   A curve has equation $y = f(x)$, where $dy/dx = 4(1-x)$.
    The curve passes through the point A, with coordinates (2, 6).

   (i)   Find the equation of the curve.   [4]

   (ii) Sketch the graph of $y = f(x)$.   [3]

   (iii) Find the equation of the normal to the curve at A.   [2]

(i) | *Time to Integrate*

'Find the equation of the curve.'

Well let me see... you're given dy/dx but not y...
I'd wager that you have to integrate that one, my friend.

You've got a bracket in the way,
so multiply that out first, to get
each term as a power of x:

$$\frac{dy}{dx} = 4(1-x)$$
$$= 4 - 4x$$

Don't forget that ol' favourite
rule for powers of x:

$$\int x^n dx = \frac{x^{n+1}}{n+1} + c$$

Now integrate each side. This will change dy/dx into y.

$$\int 4 - 4x \; dx = 4x - \frac{4x^2}{2} + c$$

Don't forget the constant of integration.

$$y = 4x - 2x^2 + c$$

I repeat — don't forget the
constant of integration.

Now you can work out what the value of c is using the known coordinate, (2, 6):

You can substitute these values of x and y into the equation you've got so far.

At A:

$x = 2$ and $y = 6$
$y = 4x - 2x^2 + c$
$6 = 4 \times 2 - 2 \times 2^2 + c$
$6 = 8 - 8 + c$
$c = 6$

So that gives:

$y = 4x - 2x^2 + 6$

(ii) | *OK class — crayons out...*

'Sketch the graph of $y = f(x)$.'

It's a quadratic, like you've seen a million times before — so you should know the shape.
But you still need to know:

1) the stationary point
2) whether it's a maximum or minimum
3) any points where it cuts the axes

Paper 1 Q7 — Integration and Graphs

1) You've already got dy/dx, so it's a quick job working out the stationary point.

> Remember that dy/dx is the rate of change of the graph. It tells you the gradient at a given point.

$$\frac{dy}{dx} = 4 - 4x$$

At a stationary point:

$$\frac{dy}{dx} = 0 \Rightarrow 4 - 4x = 0$$
$$4 = 4x$$
$$x = 1$$

And substituting $x = 1$ into the equation for y gives:

$$y = 4x - 2x^2 + 6$$
$$= 4 \times 1 - 2 \times 1^2 + 6$$
$$= 4 - 2 + 6 = 8$$

So the stationary point is at: $(1, 8)$

2) Maximum or minimum? — Look at the sign of the x^2 term.

You've got $y = 4x - 2x^2 + 6$, which has negative x^2 term — so you know that the parabola will be n-shaped instead of u-shaped.
In other words, **(1, 8)** is a **maximum**.

3) All that's left is to find the points where it cuts the axes.

Where it cuts the y-axis, $x = 0$. That gives:
$$y = 4x - 2x^2 + 6$$
$$y = 4 \times 0 - 2 \times 0^2 + 6$$
$$y = 6$$

So it crosses the y-axis at: $(0, 6)$

Where it cuts the x-axis, $y = 0$. That gives:
$$y = 4x - 2x^2 + 6$$
$$0 = 4x - 2x^2 + 6$$

Rearrange to give a positive x^2: $2x^2 - 4x - 6 = 0$
$$2(x^2 - 2x - 3) = 0$$

Factorise this to work out the x-values: $2(x + 1)(x - 3) = 0$

So the solutions will be at: $x = -1$ and $x = 3$

...which means the curve crosses the x-axis at: $(-1, 0)$ and $(3, 0)$

And that's enough information for you to do the sketch:

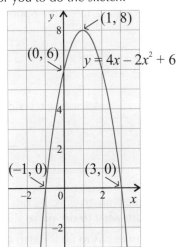

(iii) Remember the Gradient Rule

'Find the equation of the normal to the curve at A.'

The normal at A is the line at right angles to the tangent. You need to remember the gradient rule, which works for all perpendicular lines:

The gradients of two perpendicular lines multiply together to make –1.

To find the gradient of the tangent at $(2, 6)$, you can just substitute $x = 2$ into the expression for dy/dx.

$$\frac{dy}{dx} = 4 - 4x$$
$$\frac{dy}{dx} = 4 - 4 \times 2 = -4$$

So: –4 × the gradient of the normal = –1.

Therefore the gradient of the normal $= \dfrac{-1}{-4} = \dfrac{1}{4}$.

The easiest way to find the equation of a line when you know one point and the gradient is to use this form:

$$y - y_1 = m(x - x_1)$$

m is $\frac{1}{4}$ and (x_1, y_1) is the point on the line, A, with coordinates $(2, 6)$.

Substituting in all this gives:
$$y - 6 = \tfrac{1}{4}(x - 2)$$
$$y - 6 = \tfrac{1}{4}x - \tfrac{1}{2}$$
$$y = \tfrac{1}{4}x + 5\tfrac{1}{2} \text{ or } 4y = x + 22$$

Stationery point — where they keep the spare pens...

Integration isn't so bad — just make sure you remember the rule for powers of x, and the constant of integration.

Paper 1 Q8 — Factorising and Integrating

> **8**   A curve that passes through the point (2, 0) has derivative $dy/dx = 3x^2 + 6x - 4$.
>
> **(i)**   Show that the equation of the curve is $y = x^3 + 3x^2 - 4x - 12$. [3]
>
> **(ii)** Show that $(x + 3)$ is a factor of y. [2]
>
> **(iii)** Express y as a product of 3 linear factors. [2]

(i) Integrate dy/dx to find y

'A curve that passes through the point (2, 0) has derivative $dy/dx = 3x^2 + 6x - 4$.
   i) Show that the equation of the curve is $y = x^3 + 3x^2 - 4x - 12$.'

When you see dy/dx, it's easy to think "aha — differentiation!".

But in this question, you're told dy/dx and you have to work **backwards** to find y.
So you have to do the **opposite** and **integrate**.

$$\frac{dy}{dx} = 3x^2 + 6x - 4$$

Integrate each side:
$$y = \frac{3x^3}{3} + \frac{6x^2}{2} - 4x + c$$
$$y = x^3 + 3x^2 - 4x + c$$

Don't forget the constant when you integrate.

The question gives you 2 bits of info — dy/dx and a set of coordinates. If you're not sure what to do, make sure you've tried to use all the info you've been given.

The curve has to go through (2, 0), so you use that to work out what c is.

Just put $x = 2$ and $y = 0$ into the equation: $y = x^3 + 3x^2 - 4x + c$.

With these 'Show that...' questions, it's really important to write down your method clearly — it's what gets you the marks.

when $x = 2$ and $y = 0$:
$$0 = 2^3 + (3 \times 2^2) - (4 \times 2) + c$$
$$0 = 8 + 12 - 8 + c$$
$$0 = 12 + c$$
so $c = -12$,

which means your equation is: $y = x^3 + 3x^2 - 4x - 12$ — which is exactly what you want.

Usually you should check your answer by differentiating to make sure you get back to where you started — but here you don't need to, because the question tells you the answer already. You're just showing that you get the same equation.

(ii) Use the Factor Theorem

'Show that $(x + 3)$ is a factor of y.'

It's on about factors — so no prizes for guessing you need the **factor theorem**.

> The factor theorem says that to show $(x + 3)$ is a factor, you need to show that putting in the value $x = -3$ makes $y = 0$.

Paper 1 Q8 — Factorising and Integrating

It's quite easy to work out, but watch out for the minus signs:

Hopefully when you stick in –3 for x, y will come out as 0:

$$y = x^3 + 3x^2 - 4x - 12$$

$$y = (-3)^3 + 3 \times (-3)^2 - 4 \times (-3) - 12$$

$$y = -27 + 27 + 12 - 12$$

$$y = 0$$

Hence $(x + 3)$ is a factor of y.

Don't rush this kind of working — slow and steady wins the race...

(iii) Now Factorise Completely

'Express y as a product of 3 linear factors.'

You know one factor of $x^3 + 3x^2 - 4x - 12$ is $(x + 3)$. To factorise completely, you have to find what you multiply $(x + 3)$ by to get $x^3 + 3x^2 - 4x - 12$.

$$(x + 3)(\ldots\ldots\ldots) = x^3 + 3x^2 - 4x - 12$$

This bracket will be quadratic (to give the 'x^3' on the RHS). The first and last terms are easy to find:

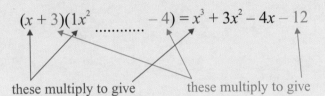

$$(x + 3)(1x^2 \ldots\ldots\ldots - 4) = x^3 + 3x^2 - 4x - 12$$

these multiply to give   these multiply to give

You can see $3 \times 1x^2$ gives the right number of x^2s and $x \times (-4)$ gives the right number of xs ...so you've actually got all you need for the second bracket.

$$(x + 3)(x^2 - 4) = x^3 + 3x^2 - 4x - 12$$

Now you need to get two factors out of $(x^2 - 4)$. Any ideas? You need to spot that it's a **difference of two squares**.

$$(x^2 - 4) = (x + 2)(x - 2)$$

You can now write y as the product of 3 linear factors:

$$y = x^3 + 3x^2 - 4x - 12 = \boxed{(x + 3)(x + 2)(x - 2)}$$

Rather elegant, I'm sure you'll agree. The algebraic equivalent of a mink coat, only slightly less controversial.

Calculus and algebra in one question — Fiendish...

I know it seems like these questions go on for ever, but I'm sure you can do all the individual bits — it's just a question of stringing it all together. But notice how the question leads you through. When it says "Show...", at least you know what you're aiming for. Aren't they good to you, those examiners... (Actually, don't answer that.)

General Certificate of Education
Advanced Subsidiary (AS) and Advanced Level

Core 1 Mathematics — Practice Exam Two

You are NOT allowed to use a calculator.

1 The function $g(x)$ is defined by $g(x) = (x-5)(x-3)(x+7)$.

   (i) Show that the rate of change of $g(x)$ with respect to x can be written $g'(x) = 3x^2 - 2x - 41$. [2]

   (ii) Hence find the x-coordinates of the stationary points of $g(x)$. [2]

   (iii) Find the ranges of x for which $g(x)$ is: (a) an increasing function of x;

                                        (b) a decreasing function of x. [3]

   (iv) If $f(x) = x^3 + 3x^2 + kx + 7$, find the possible values of k so that $f(x)$ has no turning points. [3]

2 **(i)** Rewrite the following expression in the form $f(x) = 0$, where f(x) is of the form $f(x) = ax^3 + bx^2 + cx + d$.

$$(x-1)(x^2 + x + 1) = 2x^2 - 17$$ [2]

   (ii) Show that $(x+2)$ is a factor of f(x). [2]

   (iii) Using your answer to part (ii), factorise $f(x)$ as the product of a linear factor and a quadratic factor. [3]

   (iv) Hence show that $f(x) = 0$ has no other roots. [2]

3 A new symmetrical mini-stage is to be built according to the design shown in the diagram.

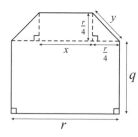

   (i) Find expressions for x and y in terms of r. [3]

   (ii) Find, in terms of r and q, expressions for the perimeter P, and the area A, of the stage. [3]

   (iii) If the perimeter of the stage is to be 40 metres, show that

       A is given by $A = 20r - \frac{r^2}{16}(9 + 4\sqrt{2})$. [3]

   (iv) By finding $\frac{dA}{dr}$ show that the maximum possible area of the stage is $A_{max} = \frac{1600}{9+4\sqrt{2}}$. [4]

4   A curve has the equation $y = f(x)$, where $f(x) = x^3 - 3x + 2$.

   (i)   Find dy/dx.   [2]

   (ii)   Find the turning points of the curve $y = f(x)$.   [4]

   (iii)   Show that $x^3 - 3x + 2$ factorises to $(x-1)^2(x+2)$.   [2]

   (iv)   Sketch the graphs of:

      (a) $y = f(x)$ [3]

      (b) $y = f(x - 3)$ [2]

      (c) $y = 2f(x)$ [2]

5   **(i)**   Solve the equation: $\dfrac{4}{(x-2)} = \dfrac{6}{(2x+5)}$.   [3]

   (ii)   Show that: $\dfrac{4}{9(x+2)} + \dfrac{1}{3(x-1)^2} + \dfrac{5}{9(x-1)} \equiv \dfrac{x^2}{(x+2)(x-1)^2}$.   [5]

6   A triangle has sides which lie on the lines given by the following equations:

      AB: $y = 3$ BC: $2x - 3y - 21 = 0$ AC: $3x + 2y - 12 = 0$

   (i)   Find the coordinates of the vertices of the triangle.   [5]

   (ii)   Show that the triangle is right-angled.   [2]

     The point D has coordinates $(3, d)$ and the point E has coordinates $(9, e)$.

   (iii)   If point D lies outside the triangle, but not on it, show that either $d > 3$ or $d < 1.5$.   [2]

   (iv)   Given that E lies inside the triangle, but not on it, find the set of possible values for e.   [3]

7   **(i)**   **(a)** Show that the graph of $f(x) = -x^2(x-2)$ has turning points at the origin and the point $\left(\frac{4}{3}, \frac{32}{27}\right)$.   [3]

      (b) Sketch the graph of $f(x)$, marking in any turning points and points where it crosses the axes.   [2]

   (ii)   The function $g(x)$ is defined by $g(x) = 2 - x$. Given that the graphs of $f(x)$ and $g(x)$ meet

     at $x = 1$, sketch the graph of $g(x)$ on the same set of axes you used in part (i), marking in the

     coordinates of the two points of intersection for which x is positive.   [3]

Paper 2 Q1 — Differentiation

1 The function $g(x)$ is defined by $g(x) = (x-5)(x-3)(x+7)$.

(i) Show that the rate of change of $g(x)$ with respect to x can be written $g'(x) = 3x^2 - 2x - 41$. [2]

(ii) Hence find the x-coordinates of the stationary points of $g(x)$. [2]

(iii) Find the ranges of x for which $g(x)$ is: **(a)** an increasing function of x;
(b) a decreasing function of x. [3]

(iv) If $f(x) = x^3 + 3x^2 + kx + 7$, find the possible values of k so that $f(x)$ has no turning points. [3]

(i) | Simplify it — then Differentiate...

'Show that the rate of change of $g(x)$ with respect to x can be written $g'(x) = 3x^2 - 2x - 41$.'

Not an easy start to the question — but the wording makes it look worse than it is. All it's asking you to do is differentiate the function. (Always differentiate to find the rate of change of something.)
And as long as you remember the rules of differentiation, it's not really that bad.

First <u>rewrite</u> g(x) so that it's in a form you can differentiate (i.e. powers of x).
$$g(x) = (x-5)(x-3)(x+7)$$
$$= (x-5)(x^2 + 4x - 21)$$
$$= x^3 - x^2 - 41x + 105$$

Then using the normal rule for differentiation...
$$g(x) = x^3 - x^2 - 41x + 105$$
$$g'(x) = \frac{dg}{dx} \Longrightarrow g'(x) = 3x^2 - 2x - 41$$

The normal rule for differentiation is...
$$\frac{d}{dx}(x^n) = nx^{n-1}$$

Got total memory loss about everything to do with differentiation? Turn to page 33 for some help.

(ii) | Find Stationary Points by setting the derivative equal to Zero

'Hence find the x-coordinates of the stationary points of $g(x)$.'

The question uses the word 'hence', so you know you have to <u>use</u> the part of the question you've already answered.

To find a <u>stationary</u> point, set the derivative equal to <u>zero</u>. Remember — the derivative shows the gradient of the curve, so the curve is flat when the derivative is zero.

You need to solve $\quad g'(x) = 0$

which is... $\quad 3x^2 - 2x - 41 = 0$

You found this in the last part of the question.

$$x = \frac{-b \pm \sqrt{b^2 - 4ac}}{2a}$$

Now this one's a nasty little beggar that can't be factorised. But don't despair — this means you can use the lovely quadratic formula.

$$x = \frac{-b \pm \sqrt{b^2 - 4ac}}{2a}$$
$$x = \frac{2 \pm \sqrt{(-2)^2 - 4 \times 3 \times (-41)}}{2 \times 3}$$
$$x = \frac{2 \pm \sqrt{496}}{6}$$
$$x = \frac{2 \pm 4\sqrt{31}}{6}$$

$3x^2 - 2x - 41 = 0$, so $a = 3$, $b = -2$, and $c = -41$

Since $\sqrt{496} = \sqrt{31} \times \sqrt{16}$.

So you get the answers... $\quad x = \dfrac{1 + 2\sqrt{31}}{3} \quad$ and $\quad x = \dfrac{1 - 2\sqrt{31}}{3}$

Paper 2 Q1 — Differentiation

(iii) Find what a function is **Doing** by drawing a **Graph**

'Find the ranges of x for which $g(x)$ is: **(a)** an increasing function of x;'

To find where a function is increasing, you need to find where the derivative is positive.

The derivative is: $g'(x) = 3x^2 - 2x - 41$.

The easiest way to find where this is positive or negative is to draw the graph of $y = g'(x) = 3x^2 - 2x - 41$ (the derivative):

It's a u-shaped parabola, and you've just found where this crosses the x-axis — at $x = \frac{1-2\sqrt{31}}{3}$ and $x = \frac{1+2\sqrt{31}}{3}$.

From the graph, you can see that $y = 3x^2 - 2x - 41$ (and therefore $g'(x)$) is positive for $x < \frac{1-2\sqrt{31}}{3}$ and $x > \frac{1+2\sqrt{31}}{3}$.

And so the function is increasing for $x < \frac{1-2\sqrt{31}}{3}$ and $x > \frac{1+2\sqrt{31}}{3}$

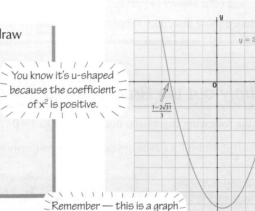

You know it's u-shaped because the coefficient of x^2 is positive.

Remember — this is a graph of $y = g'(x)$, not $y = g(x)$.

'**(b)** a decreasing function of x.'

If a function's increasing where the derivative is positive, it must be decreasing when the derivative's negative.

Using the same graph, you can see that $3x^2 - 2x - 41$ $(g'(x))$ is negative when x is between $\frac{1-2\sqrt{31}}{3}$ and $\frac{1+2\sqrt{31}}{3}$.

So the function is decreasing for $\frac{1-2\sqrt{31}}{3} < x < \frac{1+2\sqrt{31}}{3}$

(iv) If f(x) has **no Stationary Points**, then f'(x) **Cannot equal Zero**

'If $f(x) = x^3 + 3x^2 + kx + 7$, find the possible values of k so that $f(x)$ has no turning points.'

Nearly there — don't let it beat you now... It's a question about turning points, so you're going to have to differentiate. You know that stationary points only occur when the derivative (gradient) is zero, so you'll have to make sure the derivative can never be equal to zero.

It's easy enough to differentiate — just use the normal rules...

$$f(x) = x^3 + 3x^2 + kx + 7$$
$$\Rightarrow f'(x) = 3x^2 + 6x + k$$

And now it should all start to make sense — this derivative's a quadratic. You've got to make sure it's never 0. This is where the 'discriminant' (that's the '$b^2 - 4ac$' thing) comes in dead handy.

Want to know why this works? Have a look at page 15.

For a quadratic to have no roots, you need: $b^2 - 4ac < 0$

Here, a = 3, b = 6 and c = k. So you need:

$$6^2 - (4 \times 3 \times k) < 0$$
$$\Rightarrow 36 - 12k < 0$$
$$\Rightarrow 36 < 12k$$
$$\Rightarrow k > 3$$

And so f(x) will have no turning points as long as $k > 3$.

Reason number 10 — maths won't ever dump you...

This looks like quite a tricky question. Not only is the equation complicated, but it's pretty difficult to work out what the examiner actually wants you to do. But really, this question is loads of simple stuff, all bunged together, a bit like making bread. Well... not at all like making bread really... nothing like it... I'm just... ooh.. er.. you still there?.. Taxi...

Paper 2 Q2 — Algebra

2 **(i)** Rewrite the following expression in the form $f(x) = 0$, where $f(x)$ is of the form $f(x) = ax^3 + bx^2 + cx + d$.

$$(x-1)(x^2 + x + 1) = 2x^2 - 17$$

[2]

(ii) Show that $(x+2)$ is a factor of $f(x)$. [2]

(iii) Using your answer to part (ii), factorise $f(x)$ as the product of a linear factor and a quadratic factor. [3]

(iv) Hence show that $f(x) = 0$ has no other roots. [2]

(i) **Multiply** out the **Brackets** and get everything on one side

'Rewrite the following expression in the form $f(x) = 0$...'

Looks confusing, but all it's asking you to do is multiply out the brackets and then rearrange it to get <u>zero</u> on one side.

Start by multiplying out the tricky bit:

$$(x-1)(x^2 + x + 1) = x(x^2 + x + 1) - 1(x^2 + x + 1)$$
$$= x^3 + x^2 + x - x^2 - x - 1$$
$$= x^3 - 1$$

Write out the thing you're starting from:

$$(x-1)(x^2 + x + 1) = 2x^2 - 17$$

You've just worked out this bit:

$$\Rightarrow x^3 - 1 = 2x^2 - 17$$
$$\Rightarrow x^3 - 2x^2 + 16 = 0$$

... and take everything over to one side.

This is in the form f(x) = 0, if f(x) is:

$$f(x) = x^3 - 2x^2 + 16$$

... and f(x) is in the form ax³ + bx² + cx + d...

$a = 1 \quad b = -2$
$c = 0 \quad d = 16$

... so your answer is: $x^3 - 2x^2 + 16 = 0$

(ii) Show that something's a **Factor** — you need the **Factor Theorem**

'Show that $(x+2)$ is a factor of $f(x)$.'

Whenever you see the word 'factor' in a question — think '<u>Factor Theorem</u>'.
There's ALWAYS a question on it. Which is good — cos it's easy.

See page 16 for more about the Fabulous Factor Theorem.

To show whether (x + 2) is a factor of f(x), find f(–2)...

$$f(x) = x^3 - 2x^2 + 16$$
$$\Rightarrow f(-2) = (-2)^3 - 2 \times (-2)^2 + 16$$
$$= -8 - 8 + 16$$
$$= 0$$

Since f(–2) = 0, by the Factor Theorem, (x + 2) must be a factor of f(x).

The Factor Theorem   (in case you've forgotten it...)

The Factor Theorem says that (x – a) is a factor of a polynomial f(x) if and only if f(a) = 0.

So if you want to show that (x+2) is a factor of f(x), just show that f(–2) = 0.

But don't get the plus and minus signs confused...

To prove that (x+a) is a factor, show f(–a) = 0. To prove that (x–a) is a factor, show f(a) = 0.

Paper 2 Q2 — Algebra

(iii) Now you need to Factorise a Cubic

'Using your answer to part (ii), factorise *f(x)* as the product of a linear factor and a quadratic factor.'

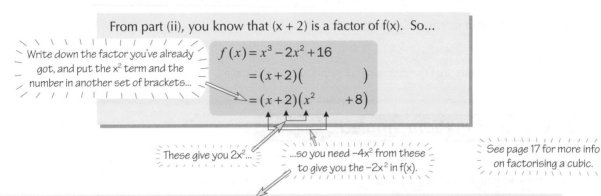

From part (ii), you know that (x + 2) is a factor of f(x). So...

Write down the factor you've already got, and put the x² term and the number in another set of brackets...

$$f(x) = x^3 - 2x^2 + 16$$
$$= (x+2)(\qquad)$$
$$= (x+2)(x^2 \qquad +8)$$

These give you 2x²...

...so you need –4x² from these to give you the –2x² in f(x).

See page 17 for more info on factorising a cubic.

So put the –4x you need in the middle of the quadratic term and you get: $f(x) = (x+2)(x^2 - 4x + 8)$

(iv) A quadratic has no real roots if its Discriminant < 0

'Hence show that f(*x*) = 0 has no other roots.'

Now you've factorised f(x), the next bit's a doddle.

$$f(x) = (x+2)(x^2 - 4x + 8)$$
so $f(x) = 0$ when $(x+2) = 0$ or $(x^2 - 4x + 8) = 0$.

You've already shown that f(x) = 0 when x + 2 = 0.

So, to show that f(x) = 0 doesn't have any <u>other</u> roots, you need to show that x² – 4x + 8 <u>is never zero</u> — i.e. x² – 4x + 8 = 0 has <u>no real roots</u>.

Now finding the number of roots can mean only one thing — calculating the <u>discriminant</u> of x² – 4x + 8. If this is <u>less than zero</u>, then x² – 4x + 8 = 0 has no real roots.

Here $a = 1$, $b = -4$ and $c = 8$.

If $b^2 - 4ac < 0$, then x² – 4x + 8 has no real roots.

$$b^2 - 4ac$$
$$= (-4)^2 - 4 \times 1 \times 8$$
$$= 16 - 32$$
$$= -16$$

Since the discriminant is less than zero, x² – 4x + 8 = 0 has no real roots, and so x² – 4x + 8 can never be zero. So that means that <u>f(x)=0 has no other solutions</u>.

Now you've finished the question. You star!

Well actually, I did the question and you just read it. So you're only a little star.

That's you that is.

The question's over — Am I not merciful... AM I NOT MERCIFUL...?

The main thing to take from this page is that the Factor Theorem will definitely be in your exam. I kid you not — it'll be there. And I reckon anyone who knew that would definitely make sure they knew what the Factor Theorem was all about before the exam — especially since it's not even that hard. Think about it — guaranteed marks on a plate. Can't be bad.

Paper 2 Q3 — Application of Calculus

3 A new symmetrical mini-stage is to be built according to the design shown in the diagram.

  (i) Find expressions for x and y in terms of r.   **[3]**

  (ii) Find, in terms of r and q, expressions for the perimeter P, and the area A, of the stage.   **[3]**

  (iii) If the perimeter of the stage is to be 40 metres, show that

    A is given by $A = 20r - \frac{r^2}{16}\left(9 + 4\sqrt{2}\right)$.   **[3]**

  (iv) By finding $\frac{dA}{dr}$ show that the maximum possible area of the stage is $A_{\max} = \dfrac{1600}{9 + 4\sqrt{2}}$.   **[4]**

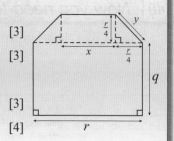

(i) Easy stuff with **Right-Angled** triangles

'Find expressions for x and y in terms of r.'

It's easier if you <u>just look at the bit</u> of the thing you're interested in.

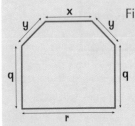

You know that the stage is symmetrical, so you can see that

$$r = x + \frac{r}{4} + \frac{r}{4}$$ ...which rearranges to... $$x = \frac{r}{2}$$

If it helps to make it clearer, redraw the bit of the diagram you need.

And using Pythagoras' theorem on the top right triangle, you can show:

Pythagoras' Theorem:
The square of the longest side equals the squares of the other two sides added together.

$$y^2 = \left(\frac{r}{4}\right)^2 + \left(\frac{r}{4}\right)^2$$
$$\Rightarrow y^2 = 2\left(\frac{r^2}{16}\right) = \frac{r^2}{8}$$
$$\Rightarrow y = \sqrt{\frac{r^2}{8}} = \frac{r}{\sqrt{8}} = \frac{r}{2\sqrt{2}}$$

$\sqrt{\frac{a}{b}} = \frac{\sqrt{a}}{\sqrt{b}}$

(See page 2 for more about surds.)

$\sqrt{8} = \sqrt{4 \times 2} = \sqrt{4} \times \sqrt{2} = 2\sqrt{2}$

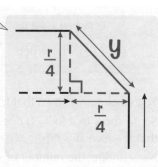

(ii) Find the **Area** and **Perimeter**

'Find, in terms of r and q, expressions for the perimeter P, and the area A, of the stage.'

Again, it'll probably help if you draw a picture so you can get a better idea of what's going on.
Do the perimeter first — it's usually easier:

First, write down the total of all the bits: $P = x + 2y + r + 2q$

You already know x and y in terms of r — so use them to simplify this.

So the total <u>perimeter</u> P is: $P = \frac{r}{2} + \frac{r}{\sqrt{2}} + r + 2q$

$y = \frac{r}{2\sqrt{2}}$, so $2y = \frac{r}{\sqrt{2}}$

$$= r\left(\frac{1}{2} + \frac{1}{\sqrt{2}} + 1\right) + 2q$$
$$= r\left(\frac{3}{2} + \frac{1}{\sqrt{2}}\right) + 2q$$

This is in terms of r and q, like the question asks for.

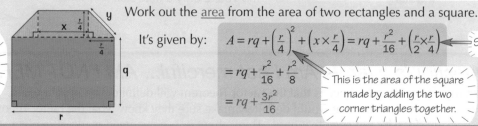

Work out the <u>area</u> from the area of two rectangles and a square.

It's given by:
$$A = rq + \left(\frac{r}{4}\right)^2 + \left(x \times \frac{r}{4}\right) = rq + \frac{r^2}{16} + \left(\frac{r}{2} \times \frac{r}{4}\right)$$

Since $x = \frac{r}{2}$.

$$= rq + \frac{r^2}{16} + \frac{r^2}{8}$$
$$= rq + \frac{3r^2}{16}$$

You can add the two corner triangles together to make a square with sides of length $\frac{r}{4}$.

This is the area of the square made by adding the two corner triangles together.

Paper 2 Q3 — Application of Calculus

(iii) Put in the Value for P — then Fiddle About a bit

'If the perimeter of the stage is to be 40 metres, show that A is given by $A = 20r - \frac{r^2}{16}\left(15 + 4\sqrt{2}\right)$.'

The question gives you a value for P, so stick that in your equation for the perimeter.

A Substitute for P in the perimeter equation, and then rearrange to get q in terms of r...

$P = 40 \Rightarrow 40 = r\left(\frac{3}{2} + \frac{1}{\sqrt{2}}\right) + 2q$

You could rearrange this to get q in terms of r, or r in terms of q. But you need to substitute for q in the equation for A.

$\Rightarrow 2q = 40 - r\left(\frac{3}{2} + \frac{1}{\sqrt{2}}\right)$

$\Rightarrow q = 20 - r\left(\frac{3}{4} + \frac{1}{2\sqrt{2}}\right)$

B And then substitute q into the equation for the area.

$A = rq + \frac{3r^2}{16}$

$= r\left\{20 - r\left(\frac{3}{4} + \frac{1}{2\sqrt{2}}\right)\right\} + \frac{3r^2}{16}$

$= 20r - r^2\left(\frac{3}{4} + \frac{1}{2\sqrt{2}} - \frac{3}{16}\right)$

Watch for sign changes if you take something negative out as a common factor.

C Rearranging the equation for the area gives you:

$A = 20r - r^2\left(\frac{3}{4} + \frac{1}{2\sqrt{2}} - \frac{3}{16}\right)$

Put all this over the common denominator $16\sqrt{2}$.

$= 20r - r^2\left\{\frac{(3 \times 4\sqrt{2}) + (1 \times 8) - (3 \times \sqrt{2})}{16\sqrt{2}}\right\}$

$= 20r - \frac{r^2}{16}\left(\frac{9\sqrt{2} + 8}{\sqrt{2}}\right)$

$\frac{8}{\sqrt{2}} = \frac{4 \times \sqrt{2} \times \sqrt{2}}{\sqrt{2}}$

$= 20r - \frac{r^2}{16}\left(9 + \frac{8}{\sqrt{2}}\right) \Rightarrow A = 20r - \frac{r^2}{16}\left(9 + 4\sqrt{2}\right)$

(iv) And finally, Maximise a Quadratic

'By finding $\frac{dA}{dr}$ show that the maximum possible area of the stage is $A_{max} = \frac{1600}{9 + 4\sqrt{2}}$.'

'By finding $\frac{dA}{dr}$' — that's a hint if ever I saw one. That's the gradient — and you know that when the gradient is zero, it's a stationary point (come on... you DO know that...).

From part (iii) you know that: $A = 20r - \frac{r^2}{16}\left(9 + 4\sqrt{2}\right)$

Differentiating gives you: $\frac{dA}{dr} = 20 - \frac{r}{8}\left(9 + 4\sqrt{2}\right)$

When you differentiate this, you get $\frac{dA}{dr}$ (not $\frac{dy}{dx}$), since you've got a formula for A and you're differentiating with respect to r.

Now A is a maximum when $\frac{dA}{dr} = 0$, and this is when:

$20 - \frac{r}{8}\left(9 + 4\sqrt{2}\right) = 0$

Don't stop here — this is just the value of r that maximises A. You need the actual maximum value of A.

$\Rightarrow r = \frac{8 \times 20}{9 + 4\sqrt{2}} = \frac{160}{9 + 4\sqrt{2}}$

So put this value of r back into the expression for A to find that the maximum value of A is:

Put your value of r into the equation for A....

$A_{max} = 20 \times \left(\frac{160}{9 + 4\sqrt{2}}\right) - \frac{1}{16}\left(\frac{160}{9 + 4\sqrt{2}}\right)^2\left(9 + 4\sqrt{2}\right)$

...play about very carefully,...

$= \left(\frac{3200}{9 + 4\sqrt{2}}\right) - \frac{1}{16} \cdot \frac{160^2 \cdot (9 + 4\sqrt{2})}{(9 + 4\sqrt{2})^2}$

Cancel a $9 + 4\sqrt{2}$ from the top and bottom lines.

...and all this mess should suddenly begin to look more friendly.

$= \left(\frac{3200}{9 + 4\sqrt{2}}\right) - \left(\frac{1600}{9 + 4\sqrt{2}}\right) = \frac{1600}{9 + 4\sqrt{2}}$

There. That wasn't so bad, was it? Was it? Hello? Hello? Hellooo... Doctor! Somebody call a doctor...

Differentiate — and the world differentiates with you...

That's often the way with these longer questions — they try to guide you through what you're supposed to do, and one big, difficult question becomes a few smaller, easier questionettes. So don't panic if the question looks impossible when you first see it — it's probably not so bad when you get down to it. And if it's still bad when you get down to it, use the Force...

Paper 2 Q4 — Differentiation and Graphs

> 4   A curve has the equation $y = f(x)$, where $f(x) = x^3 - 3x + 2$.
>
> **(i)** Find dy/dx. [2]
>
> **(ii)** Find the turning points of the curve $y = f(x)$. [4]
>
> **(iii)** Show that $x^3 - 3x + 2$ factorises to $(x - 1)^2(x + 2)$. [2]
>
> **(iv)** Sketch the graphs of:
>
> **(a)** $y = f(x)$ [3]
>
> **(b)** $y = f(x - 3)$ [2]
>
> **(c)** $y = 2f(x)$ [2]

(i) Use the Rule for Differentiation

'Find dy/dx.'

For powers of x you multiply by the power then drop the power by 1.

And you do that for each term.

$$y = x^3 - 3x + 2$$

$2 = 2 \times 1 = 2x^0$ — which differentiates to give 0.

$$\frac{dy}{dx} = 3x^{3-1} - 3x^{1-1} + 0$$

$x^0 = 1$

$$= 3x^2 - 3$$

(ii) Put dy/dx = 0

'Find the turning points of the curve $y = f(x)$.'

The turning points are where $dy/dx = 0$. You've just worked out dy/dx — so just set that equal to 0:

You can take a factor of 3 out, leaving:

$$3x^2 - 3 = 0$$
$$x^2 - 1 = 0$$

You've got 'x^2 – a number', so you can use the difference of two squares:

$$(x + 1)(x - 1) = 0$$

Putting each bracket equal to 0 gives the solutions:

$$x = -1 \text{ and } x = 1$$

The question asks for the points, so you've got to give coordinates. That means you need the y-values as well:

When $x = -1$:
$$y = x^3 - 3x + 2$$
$$= (-1)^3 - (3 \times -1) + 2$$
$$= -1 + 3 + 2$$
$$= 4$$

When $x = 1$:
$$y = x^3 - 3x + 2$$
$$= 1^3 - (3 \times 1) + 2$$
$$= 1 - 3 + 2$$
$$= 0$$

So the turning points are at: $(-1, 4)$ and $(1, 0)$.

(iii) Don't make a meal of this...

'Show that $x^3 - 3x + 2$ factorises to $(x - 1)^2(x + 2)$.'

You've been given all the factors, so the easiest way to check they're right is to multiply them out.

Start by expanding $(x - 1)^2$.

When you square a bracket, it's a good idea to write it out in full, otherwise you might forget about the terms in x.

Or you could use the Factor Theorem

$$(x - 1)^2 = (x - 1)(x - 1)$$
$$= x^2 - x - x + 1$$
$$= x^2 - 2x + 1$$

now multiply by $(x + 2)$: $(x - 1)^2(x + 2) = (x^2 - 2x + 1)(x + 2)$

multiply out RHS:
$$= x^3 + 2x^2 - 2x^2 - 4x + x + 2$$
$$= x^3 - 3x + 2$$

Stop and check — if you multiply a bracket with 3 things in by a bracket with 2 things in, you should get 6 things altogether.

And that's the right answer.

Paper 2 Q4 — Differentiation and Graphs

(iv)(a) | Sketching — at last something I'm good at...

'Sketch the graph of $y = f(x)$.'

This bit uses all of the previous bits — as is often the way with these huge, multi-part questions.

To sketch a curve, you'd ideally like to know:

> 1) any turning points
> 2) where it crosses the axes
> 3) a rough idea of the shape

1) You know that the turning points are at $(-1, 4)$ and $(1, 0)$ from part (ii).

2) You're already on your way to finding the x-intercepts, from the factorising you did for part (iii).

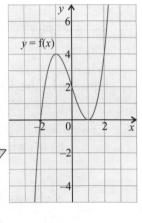

When $y = 0$: $(x - 1)^2(x + 2) = 0$
so $x = 1$ and $x = -2$

When $x = 0$: $y = x^3 - 3x + 2$
$= 0 - 0 + 2$
$= 2$

So the x-intercepts are $(1, 0)$ and $(-2, 0)$.

So the y-intercept is $(0, 2)$.

3) You should know the rough shape of a cubic graph by now, but in any case you know there are two turning points. And you (probably) also know that a cubic graph with a positive x^3 term will start low and finish high.

Putting all these together you can now sketch the graph.

(v)(b) | Translate the graph

'Sketch the graph of $y = f(x - 3)$'

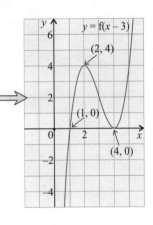

There are a few types of transformation you've just got to **learn**.
This one's pretty easy — just a simple **translation**.
The graph of $f(x - a)$ is the same as the graph of $f(x)$,
but **shifted to the right**.

> If you can't remember which way the shift goes, go back to
> $y = x$ compared with $y = x - a$. Draw yourself a thumbnail
> sketch of each one, by working out the intercepts.

(v)(c) | And 1 and 2 and... Stretch...

'Sketch the graph of $y = 2f(x)$'

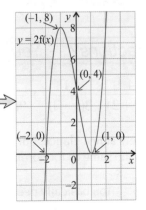

This time it's a **stretch** up the y-axis, with **scale factor 2**.
This is pretty straightforward — all you need to do is
double the y-coordinates of the original graph.

> You could do a detailed table of values, but it's enough
> just to look at the points you worked out in part (iv)(a).

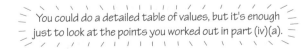

Translate 'a graph' — 'una gráfica', 'un graphique', 'ein Schaubild'...
Make sure you learn the basic transformations *before* the exam — translations, stretches, reflections and rotations.

Paper 2 Q5 — Algebraic Fractions

5 (i) Solve the equation: $\dfrac{4}{(x-2)} = \dfrac{6}{(2x+5)}$. [3]

(ii) Show that: $\dfrac{4}{9(x+2)} + \dfrac{1}{3(x-1)^2} + \dfrac{5}{9(x-1)} \equiv \dfrac{x^2}{(x+2)(x-1)^2}$. [5]

(i) Get rid of Denominators when you can

'Solve the equation: $\dfrac{4}{(x-2)} = \dfrac{6}{(2x+5)}$.'

Whenever you have equations with fractions, it's a good idea to multiply each side of the equation by the denominators.

Here's what you've got to solve: $\dfrac{4}{(x-2)} = \dfrac{6}{(2x+5)}$

You've got **2** denominators, so multiply each side by $(x-2)$ **and** $(2x+5)$.

$$\frac{4(2x+5)(x-2)}{(x-2)} = \frac{6(2x+5)(x-2)}{(2x+5)}$$

$$4(2x+5) = 6(x-2)$$

This is cross-multiplication. Multiplying by the denominators of both sides will always get rid of the fractions.

Now multiply out and solve the equation:

$$4(2x+5) = 6(x-2)$$
$$8x + 20 = 6x - 12$$
$$2x = -32$$
$$x = -16$$

Check by subbing in this value of x into original equation:
$$\frac{4}{(-16-2)} = \frac{6}{(2\times(-16)+5)}$$
$$\frac{4}{-18} = \frac{6}{-27}$$
$$-\frac{2}{9} = -\frac{2}{9} \checkmark$$

(ii) Adding fractions? — You need a Common Denominator

'Show that: $\dfrac{4}{9(x+2)} + \dfrac{1}{3(x-1)^2} + \dfrac{5}{9(x-1)} \equiv \dfrac{x^2}{(x+2)(x-1)^2}$.'

This looks unlikely at first glance, but don't let that put you off. When you add algebraic fractions, the technique is the same as for normal fractions. You need a **common denominator**.

You basically need to multiply together **all** the denominators on the LHS.
But **when one term is a factor of another term**, you only need the **larger term**.

This only really makes sense when you see it work in practice...

Paper 2 Q5 — Algebraic Fractions

Finding the common denominator:

Look at the numbers in the LHS denominators. You've got 9, 3 and 9. Well, 3 is a factor of 9, so you only need the larger term, i.e. **9**.

The next thing to take a look at is the **(x + 2)**. This term **isn't** a factor of any of the other terms on the bottom, so you **will** need this.

Then you've got $(x-1)^2$. One of the fractions has $(x-1)$ as its denominator, which is of course a factor of $(x-1)^2$. So again you just need the larger term, i.e. $(x-1)^2$.

You've now looked at all the terms in the three denominators, and the common denominator you're left with is:

$$9(x+2)(x-1)^2$$

Make the denominator of each part the common denominator:

This involves multiplying the top and bottom of each fraction by **the terms of the common denominator that aren't in the denominator of the original fraction**. I know this sounds horrendous, but it'll make more sense when you see it in action.

Look at this fraction on the left: you've already got $9(x+2)$ on the bottom, so you only need to multiply top and bottom by $(x-1)^2$.

$$\frac{4}{9(x+2)} + \frac{1}{3(x-1)^2} + \frac{5}{9(x-1)}$$

You should be able to cancel down all the new fractions back to the original fractions.

E.g. $\dfrac{5(x+2)(x-1)}{9(x+2)(x-1)^2} = \dfrac{5}{9(x-1)}$

$$= \frac{4(x-1)^2}{9(x+2)(x-1)^2} + \frac{3(x+2)}{9(x+2)(x-1)^2} + \frac{5(x+2)(x-1)}{9(x+2)(x-1)^2}$$

Now multiply out the top bits.

$$= \frac{4x^2-8x+4}{9(x+2)(x-1)^2} + \frac{3x+6}{9(x+2)(x-1)^2} + \frac{5x^2+5x-10}{9(x+2)(x-1)^2}$$

Now you can turn it into just one fraction, and then it's just a question of collecting all the like terms.

$$= \frac{4x^2-8x+4}{9(x+2)(x-1)^2} + \frac{3x+6}{9(x+2)(x-1)^2} + \frac{5x^2+5x-10}{9(x+2)(x-1)^2}$$

$$= \frac{4x^2+5x^2-8x+3x+5x+4+6-10}{9(x+2)(x-1)^2}$$

$$= \frac{9x^2}{9(x+2)(x-1)^2}$$

The 9s cancel down:

$$= \frac{x^2}{(x+2)(x-1)^2}$$

and this is what the question asks for.

'The Denominator' — starring Armando Schwarzkopf...

Algebraic fractions — I shudder at the very sight of them. The most awkward bit when you're adding them, though, is finding the lowest common denominator. If it comes to the day and you can't remember how to do it, just multiply all the denominators together and use that. It's less elegant, but it *is* a common denominator.

Paper 2 Q6 — Simultaneous Equations

> **6** A triangle has sides which lie on the lines given by the following equations:
>
>   AB: $y = 3$ BC: $2x - 3y - 21 = 0$ AC: $3x + 2y - 12 = 0$
>
> **(i)** Find the coordinates of the vertices of the triangle. [5]
>
> **(ii)** Show that the triangle is right-angled. [2]
>
> The point D has coordinates $(3, d)$ and the point E has coordinates $(9, e)$.
>
> **(iii)** If point D lies outside the triangle, but not on it, show that either $d > 3$ or $d < 1.5$. [2]
>
> **(iv)** Given that E lies inside the triangle, but not on it, find the set of possible values for e. [3]

(i) | ## Sketch the Lines before you deal with the Simultaneous Equations

'Find the coordinates of the vertices of the triangle.'

You don't *have* to draw a sketch, but sketches always help make questions like this clearer.

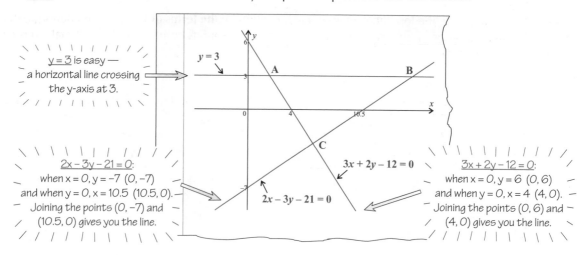

$y = 3$ is easy — a horizontal line crossing the y-axis at 3.

$2x - 3y - 21 = 0$: when $x = 0$, $y = -7$ $(0, -7)$ and when $y = 0$, $x = 10.5$ $(10.5, 0)$. Joining the points $(0, -7)$ and $(10.5, 0)$ gives you the line.

$3x + 2y - 12 = 0$: when $x = 0$, $y = 6$ $(0, 6)$ and when $y = 0$, $x = 4$ $(4, 0)$. Joining the points $(0, 6)$ and $(4, 0)$ gives you the line.

From the graph, you can see roughly where points A, B and C are, but you'll need to go through the algebra.

Finding A and B is straightforward, since you know that the y-coordinate is 3:

So for A: | $3x + 2y - 12 = 0$
$3x + (2 \times 3) - 12 = 0$
$3x + 6 - 12 = 0$
$3x = 6$
$x = 2$ — A has coordinates (2, 3).

And for B: | $2x - 3y - 21 = 0$
$2x - 3 \times 3 - 21 = 0$
$2x - 9 - 21 = 0$
$2x = 30$
$x = 15$ — B has coordinates (15, 3).

At C, you've got to solve a pair of simultaneous equations — bad luck. Label the equations: | $2x - 3y - 21 = 0$ (1)
$3x + 2y - 12 = 0$ (2)

Multiply equation (1) by 2 and equation (2) by 3 to get the coefficients of y equal:

$4x - 6y - 42 = 0$
$9x + 6y - 36 = 0$

Now add together to get rid of y:

$13x - 78 = 0$
$13x = 78$
$x = 6$

Substitute into equation (1) or (2) to find y:
Using eq. (2): | $3x + 2y - 12 = 0$ (2)
$(3 \times 6) + 2y - 12 = 0$
$18 + 2y - 12 = 0$
$2y + 6 = 0$
$2y = -6$
$y = -3$ — C has coordinates (6, −3).

These answers seem to make sense if you look back at the sketch, which is reassuring.

You should really check that works, by substituting your values into equation (1), but I'm running out of room.

Paper 2 Q6 — Simultaneous Equations

(ii) A Right Angle probably means you need the Gradient Rule

'Show that the triangle is right-angled.'

Whenever you see 'right angle' in a coordinate geometry question, remember that the <u>gradients of two perpendicular lines multiply together to make -1</u>. So if you can show that they do, you've shown the triangle must be right-angled.

To find the gradient of each line, rearrange it into the form $y = mx + c$ — and m will be the gradient.
You can tell from the diagram that the right angle looks like it's at C, so use BC and AC.

Line BC: $2x - 3y - 21 = 0$ Line AC: $3x + 2y - 12 = 0$
                 $3y = 2x - 21$ $2y = -3x + 12$

divide by 3: $y = \frac{2}{3}x - 7$ divide by 2: $y = -\frac{3}{2}x + 6$

$\Rightarrow$ You can see from the $y = mx + c$ form of the equations that the gradients are $\frac{2}{3}$ and $-\frac{3}{2}$.

$\frac{2}{3} \times -\frac{3}{2} = -1$ so the lines that meet at C are perpendicular, and the triangle must be right-angled.

(iii) You know what I'm gonna say — sketch it on your graph

'If point D lies outside the triangle, but not on it, show that either $d > 3$ or $d < 1.5$.'

Point D has co-ordinates (3, d), so it must lie on the line x = 3. It lies outside the triangle, so you can see from the sketch that it must lie **above the line AB** and **below the line AC**.

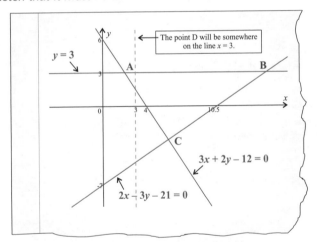

First off you can happily say that $d > 3$ is one condition, because $y = 3$ is the top of the triangle.

Secondly you have to work out the values of d that would give D below the line AC.

If D was on the line AC, then (3, d) would satisfy $3x + 2y - 12 = 0$:

$3 \times 3 + 2d - 12 = 0$
$9 + 2d - 12 = 0$
$2d - 3 = 0$
$d = 1.5$

But as D can't be on the triangle, you need the y-coordinate to be less than 1.5, i.e. $d < 1.5$.
So the conditions are $d > 3$ or $d < 1.5$.

(iv) Same thing again... almost

'Given that E lies inside the triangle, but not on it, find the set of possible values for e.'

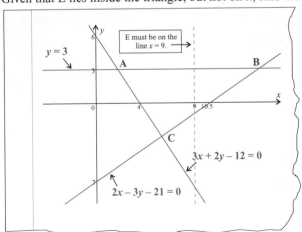

From the diagram you can tell that E is below AB and above BC. So, clearly, $e < 3$. Now work out the values of e so that E is above the line BC.

If e was on the line BC, then (9, e) would satisfy $2x - 3y - 21 = 0$:

$2x - 3y - 21 = 0$
$2 \times 9 - 3e - 21 = 0$
$18 - 3e - 21 = 0$
$-3e - 3 = 0$
$e = -1$

So above the line $e > -1$
Putting both conditions together gives you: $-1 < e < 3$

Simultaneous equations and graphs and gradients and inequalities...
These are a few of my favourite things.

Paper 2 Q7 — Integration

7 (i) (a) Show that the graph of $f(x) = -x^2(x-2)$ has turning points at the origin and the point $\left(\frac{4}{3}, \frac{32}{27}\right)$. [3]

(b) Sketch the graph of $f(x)$, marking in any turning points and points where it crosses the axes. [2]

(ii) The function $g(x)$ is defined by $g(x) = 2 - x$. Given that the graphs of $f(x)$ and $g(x)$ meet at $x = 1$, sketch the graph of $g(x)$ on the same set of axes you used in part (i), marking in the coordinates of the two points of intersection for which x is positive. [3]

(i) (a) Differentiate — and then set the derivative equal to Zero

'Show that the graph of $f(x) = -x^2(x-2)$ has turning points at the origin and the point $\left(\frac{4}{3}, \frac{32}{27}\right)$.'

Turning points occur when f'(x) = 0. So first differentiate f(x), then set the derivative to zero.

$$f(x) = -x^2(x-2)$$
$$= -x^3 + 2x^2$$

And so

$$f'(x) = -3x^2 + 2(2x^1)$$

Using the fact that $\frac{d}{dx}(x^n) = nx^{n-1}$.

$$= -3x^2 + 4x$$
$$= x(-3x + 4)$$

Factorise this so it's easy to see when it's zero.

Now put f'(x) equal to 0:

$$f'(x) = 0 \implies x(-3x+4) = 0$$
$$\implies x = 0 \text{ or } x = \frac{4}{3}$$

So there are turning points at $x = 0$ and $x = \frac{4}{3}$.

But the question asks for the actual points, so you need to find the y-coordinates too, i.e. f(0) and $f\left(\frac{4}{3}\right)$:

$$f(0) = 0, \text{ and } f\left(\frac{4}{3}\right) = -\left(\frac{4}{3}\right)^2\left(\frac{4}{3} - 2\right) = -\frac{16}{9}\left(-\frac{2}{3}\right) = \frac{32}{27}.$$

So the turning points are $(0,0)$ (i.e. the origin) and $\left(\frac{4}{3}, \frac{32}{27}\right)$.

Paper 2 Q7 — Integration

(i)(b) | Sketching f(x) — it's a **Cubic**

'Sketch the graph of $f(x)$, marking in any turning points and points where it crosses the axes.'

$$f(x) = -x^2(x-2) = -x^3 + 2x^2$$

There's basically three things you need to know to draw this graph:

1. **What shape is the graph?**
   f(x) is a cubic function, and the coefficient of x^3 is negative (–1) — so it goes from top-left to bottom-right.

   (Or you can work it out: as x goes towards $+\infty$, $-x^3$ goes towards $-\infty$ and as x goes towards $-\infty$, $-x^3$ goes towards ∞. *)*

2. **Where does it cross the x-axis?**
   Just put f(x) equal to 0:
   $$f(x) = -x^2(x-2) = 0 \implies x = 0 \text{ and } x = 2$$

3. **Where are the turning points?**

   We already know these from part i(a). Don't forget to mark them on.

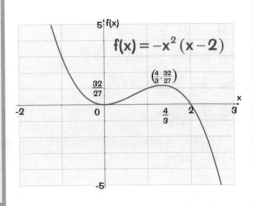

(ii) | Sketch a **Straight** line on the **Same** pair of axes

'$g(x)$ is defined by $g(x) = 2 - x$. Given that the graphs of $f(x)$ and $g(x)$ meet at $x = 1$, sketch the graph of $g(x)$ on the same set of axes you used in part (i), marking in the coordinates of the two points of intersection for which x is positive.'

You've got to stick g(x), which is just a straight line, on your graph. So all you do is plot 2 points and draw a straight line through them. The best points to choose are where it crosses the x- and y- axes.

g(x) crosses the: y-axis at y = 2 (just put x = 0), and the x-axis at x = 2 (just set g(x) = 0).

The question asks you to mark on the 2 points where f(x) and g(x) meet.

It tells you that they meet at x=1. And since $f(1) = -1^2(1-2) = 1$, the two graphs cross at the point (1,1).

You can see the other point just by looking at the graph. It's (2,0).

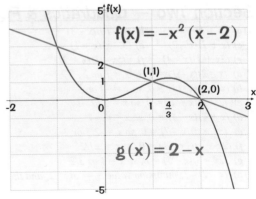

I've got a bad feeling about this...

This is a prett meaty question — but a quick think and a quick sketch before you start will be dead useful. And as long as you've had plenty of practice with the little tricks you need to use (e.g. differentiating to find turning points), you'll be all right.

Answers

Section One — Algebra Basics

1) a) *a & b are constants, x is a variable.*
 b) *k is a constant, θ is a variable.*
 c) *a, b & c are constants, y is a variable.*
 d) *a is a constant, x, y are variables*
2) *Identity symbol is ≡.*
3) *A, C and D are identities.*

4) a) $-\frac{16}{15}$
 b) *f is undefined (or ∞)*
 c) $\frac{3}{2}$
 d) *0*

5) a) $x = \pm\sqrt{5}$
 b) $x = -2 \pm \sqrt{3}$

6) a) $2\sqrt{7}$ **b)** $\frac{\sqrt{5}}{6}$ **c)** $3\sqrt{2}$ **d)** $\frac{3}{4}$

7) a) $\frac{8}{\sqrt{2}} = \frac{2\times 2\times\sqrt{2}\times\sqrt{2}}{\sqrt{2}} = 4\sqrt{2}$
 b) $\frac{\sqrt{2}}{2} = \frac{\sqrt{2}}{\left(\sqrt{2}\right)^2} = \frac{1}{\sqrt{2}}$

 (there are other possible ways to do these questions)

8) $136 + 24\sqrt{21}$

9) $3 - \sqrt{7}$

10) a) $a^2 - b^2$
 b) $a^2 + 2ab + b^2$
 c) $25y^2 + 210xy$
 d) $3x^2 + 10xy + 3y^2 + 13x + 23y + 14$

11) a) $xy(2x + a + 2y\sin x)$
 b) $\sin^2 x\left(1 + \cos^2 x\right)$
 c) $8(2y + xy + 7x)$
 d) $(x - 2)(x - 3)$

12) a) $\frac{52x + 5y}{60}$ **b)** $\frac{5x - 2y}{x^2 y^2}$ **c)** $\frac{x^3 + x^2 - y^2 + xy^2}{x\left(x^2 - y^2\right)}$

13) a) $\frac{3a}{2b}$ **b)** $\frac{2\left(p^2 + q^2\right)}{p^2 - q^2}$ **c)** 🐦 = 🌧️

Section Two — Quadratics & Polynomials

1) a) $(x + 1)^2$ **b)** $(x - 10)(x - 3)$
 c) $(x + 2)(x - 2)$ **d)** $(3 - x)(x + 1)$
 e) $(2x + 1)(x - 4)$ **f)** $(5x - 3)(x + 2)$

2) a) $(x - 2)(x - 1) = 0$, so $x = 1$ or 2
 b) $(x + 4)(x - 3) = 0$, so $x = -4$ or 3
 c) $(2 - x)(x + 1) = 0$, so $x = 2$ or -1
 d) $(x + 4)(x - 4) = 0$, so $x = 4, -4$
 e) $(3x + 2)(x - 7) = 0$, so $x = -2/3$ or 7
 f) $(2x + 1)(2x - 1) = 0$, so $x = \pm 1/2$
 g) $(2x - 3)(x - 1) = 0$, so $x = 1$ or $3/2$

3) a) $(x - 2)^2 - 7$; minimum value $= -7$ at $x=2$, and this crosses the x-axis at $x = 2 \pm \sqrt{7}$
 b) $\frac{21}{4} - \left(x + \frac{3}{2}\right)^2$; maximum value $= 21/4$ at $x = -3/2$, and this crosses the x-axis at $x = -\frac{3}{2} \pm \sqrt{\frac{21}{4}}$
 c) $2(x - 1)^2 + 9$; minimum value $= 9$ at $x = 1$, and this doesn't cross the x-axis.
 d) $4\left(x - \frac{7}{2}\right)^2 - 1$; minimum value $= -1$ at $x = 7/2$, crosses the x-axis at $x = \frac{7}{2} \pm \frac{1}{\sqrt{2}}$.

4) a) $b^2 - 4ac = 16$, so 2 roots
 b) $b^2 - 4ac = 0$, so 1 root
 c) $b^2 - 4ac = -8$, so no roots

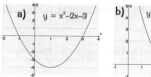
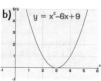

5) a) $x = \frac{7 \pm \sqrt{13}}{6}$
 b) $x = \frac{3 \pm \sqrt{13}}{2}$
 c) $x = -2 \pm \sqrt{10}$

6) $k^2 - (4 \times 1 \times 4) > 0$, so $k^2 > 16$ and so $k > 4$ or $k < -4$.

7) a) $x^2 - 4x + 14$, remainder -16
 b) $3x^2 + 10x + 8$, remainder 7.

8) Put $x = -2$. $x^3 + 5x^2 + 2x - 8 = -8 + 20 - 4 - 8 = 0$
 So by the Factor Theorem, $(x + 2)$ is a factor.

9) a) $(3x - 1)$ Put $x = \frac{1}{3} \Rightarrow 3x^3 + 23x^2 + 37x - 15$
 $= \frac{3}{27} + \frac{23}{9} + \frac{37}{3} - 15$
 $= \frac{135}{9} - 15 = 0$
 so by the Factor Theorem, $\left(x - \frac{1}{3}\right)$ or $(3x - 1)$ is a factor.
 b) $(x - 1)(x - 2)(x + 2)$

Section Three — Simultaneous Equations and Inequalities

1) a) $x > -\frac{38}{5}$ **b)** $y \leq \frac{7}{8}$ **c)** $y \leq -\frac{3}{4}$
2) (i) $x > 5/2$ (ii) $x > -4$ (iii) $x \leq -3$
3) a) $-\frac{1}{3} \leq x \leq 2$
 b) $x < 1 - \sqrt{3}$ or $x > 1 + \sqrt{3}$
 c) $x \leq -3$ or $x \geq -2$
4) (i) $x \leq -3$ and $x \geq 1$ (ii) $x < -1/2$ and $x > 1$ (iii) $-3 < x < 2$
5) a) $(-3, -4)$
 b) $\left(-\frac{1}{6}, -\frac{5}{12}\right)$
6) a) The line and curve meet at the points $(2, -6)$ and $(7, 4)$.
 b) The line is a tangent to the parabola at the point $(2, 26)$.
 c) The equations have no solution and so the line and the curve never meet.
7) a) $\left(\frac{1}{4}, -\frac{13}{4}\right)$ **b)** $(4, 5)$ **c)** $(-5, -2)$

Section Four — Coordinate Geometry and Graphs

1) a) (i) $y + 1 = 3(x - 2)$ (ii) $y = 3x - 7$ (iii) $3x - y - 7 = 0$
 b) (i) $y + \frac{1}{3} = \frac{1}{5}x$ (ii) $y = \frac{1}{5}x - \frac{1}{3}$ (iii) $3x - 15y - 5 = 0$
2) a) $\left(-\frac{1}{2}, 1\right)$
 b) $\left(6, \frac{15}{2}\right)$
 c) $\left(\frac{199}{2}, \frac{17}{2}\right)$
3) a) $2\sqrt{58}$
 b) $2\sqrt{61}$

Answers

4) a) $y = \frac{3}{2}x - 4$

b) $y = -\frac{1}{2}x + 4$

5) D is the point $\left(\frac{7}{2}, 7\right)$. So the line passing through AD is
$y = \frac{6}{5}x + \frac{14}{5} = \frac{1}{5}(6x + 14)$.

6) The midpoint of RS is $\left(5, \frac{13}{2}\right)$. The equation of the required line is
$y = \frac{8}{7}x + \frac{11}{14}$.

7) a) 3, (0, 0) **b)** 2, (2, –4) **c)** 5, (–3, 4)

8)
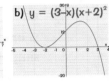
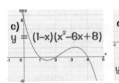
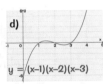

Section Five — Differentiation

1) $\frac{d}{dx}\left(x^n\right) = nx^{n-1}$

2) a) $\frac{dy}{dx} = 2x$, 2

b) $\frac{dy}{dx} = 4x^3 + 5$, 9

c) $\frac{dy}{dx} = 15(x^2 + 1)$, 30

3) They're the same.

4) a) $\frac{dy}{dx} = 12x - 6$, so function is increasing when $x > 0.5$, and decreasing when $x < 0.5$.

b) $\frac{dy}{dx} = 3x^2 - 12$, so there are turning points at $x = 2$ and $x = -2$. So function is increasing when $x < -2$ and when $x > 2$. Function is decreasing when $-2 < x < 2$.

5) A point where $\frac{dy}{dx} = 0$. $y = x^3 - 5x^2 + 4x \Rightarrow \frac{dy}{dx} = 3x^2 - 10x + 4$, so stationary points are at $x = \frac{10 \pm \sqrt{52}}{6}$

6) Differentiate again to find $\frac{d^2y}{dx^2}$. If this is positive, stationary point is a minimum; if it's negative, stationary point is a maximum.

7) $\frac{dy}{dx} = 3x^2 + 6x$; this is zero at (0, 0) and (–2, 4). $\frac{d^2y}{dx^2} = 6x + 6$; at $x = 0$ this is positive, so (0, 0) is a minimum; at $x = -2$ this is negative, so (–2, 4) is a maximum.

8) Stationary points are (1, –2) (minimum) and (–1, 2) (maximum).

Section Six — Integration

1) i) Increase the power of x by 1, ii) divide by the new power, iii) add a constant. (Or substitute in limits and subtract for a definite integral)

2) An integral without limits to integrate between. Because there's more than one right answer.

3) Differentiate your answer, and if you get back the function you integrated in the first place, your answer's right.

4) **a)** $2x^5 + C$ **b)** $\frac{3x^2}{2} + \frac{5x^3}{3} + C$ **c)** $\frac{3}{4}x^4 + \frac{2}{3}x^3 + C$

5) Integrating gives $y = 3x^2 - 7x + C$; then substitute $x=1$ and $y=0$ to find that $C = 4$. So the equation of the curve is $y = 3x^2 - 7x + 4$.

6) Integrate to get $y = \frac{3x^4}{4} - 2x + C$. Putting $x=1$ and $y=0$ gives $C = -\frac{11}{4}$, and so the required curve is $y = \frac{3x^4}{4} + 2x - \frac{11}{4}$. If the curve has to go through (1, 2) instead of (1, 0), substitute the values $x=1$ and $y=2$ to find a different value for C, call this value C_1. Making these substitutions gives $C_1 = -\frac{3}{4}$, and the equation of the new curve is $y = \frac{3x^4}{4} + 2x - \frac{3}{4}$.

7) Check whether there are limits to integrate between. If there are, then it's a definite integral; if not, it's an indefinite integral.

8) The area between the curve $y = f(x)$ and the x-axis, between $x = a$ and $x = b$.

9) a) $\int_{-3}^{3}(9 - x^2)dx = \left[9x - \frac{x^3}{3}\right]_{-3}^{3} = 18 - (-18) = 36$

b) $\int_{1}^{9}\frac{3+x}{4}dx = \left[\frac{3}{4}x + \frac{x^2}{8}\right]_{1}^{9} = 16$

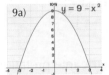
9a) $y = 9 - x^2$

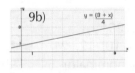
9b) $y = \frac{(3+x)}{4}$

10) a) $\int_{0}^{1}(4x^3 + 3x^2 + 2x + 1)dx$
$= \left[x^4 + x^3 + x^2 + x\right]_{0}^{1}$
$= 4 - 0 = 4$

b) $\int_{1}^{2}(10x^5 + 8x^2)dx = \left[\frac{10x^6}{6} + \frac{8x^3}{3}\right]_{1}^{2}$
$= \left(\frac{320}{3} + \frac{64}{3}\right) - \left(\frac{5}{3} + \frac{8}{3}\right) = \frac{371}{3}$

11) a) $A = \int_{2}^{3}(x^3 - 5x^2 + 6x)dx$
$= \left[\frac{x^4}{4} - \frac{5}{3}x^3 + 3x^2\right]_{2}^{3} = -\frac{5}{12} \Rightarrow Area = \frac{5}{12}$

b) $A = \int_{0}^{2}2x^2dx + \int_{2}^{6}(12 - 2x)dx$
$= \left[\frac{2}{3}x^3\right]_{0}^{2} + \left[12x - x^2\right]_{2}^{6}$
$= \frac{16}{3} + 16 = \frac{64}{3}$

c) $A = \int_{1}^{3}(x^2 - 4x + 7)dx$
$= \left[\frac{x^3}{3} - 2x^2 + 7x\right]_{1}^{3}$
$= \frac{20}{3}$ (Note : The line $y = 4$ is a red herring. Ha ha.)

Index